Donald B. Louria. M.D.

The Drug Scene

CORGI BOOKS
TRANSWORLD PUBLISHERS LTD
A National General Company

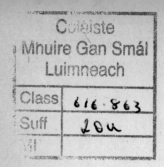

THE DRUG SCENE

A CORGI BOOK 552 08594 4

First publication in Great Britain

PRINTING HISTORY
Corgi edition published 1970

Copyright © 1968 by Donald B. Louria

This book is set in 10/11 pt. Times

Corgi Books are published by Transworld Publishers Ltd.,
Cavendish House, 57–59 Uxbridge Road,
Ealing, London, W.5.
Made and printed in Great Britain by
Hunt Barnard Printing Ltd., Aylesbury, Bucks.

To Barbara—a gem by any criterion

CONTENTS

INTRODUCTION

Every month or two a new hardcover or paperback book appears on the subject of drug use in our society. At present there are probably more people writing about LSD and other potent drugs than there are persons actually dedicated to doing something about our burgeoning drug problem. Having written a manual one and a half years ago which summarized the drug abuse situation, I hesitate to add further to an already overburdened literature. But it does seem to me that this is a propitious time to analyze the drug scene.

We have learned an enormous amount about many of the newer drugs during the last two years, and statistical data are now available on prevalence and trends in drug abuse. Then, too, the initial thrust of the psychedelic cult appears to have lost a great deal of its vigor; now is the perfect time to survey the recent past and by so doing to suggest some reasonable approaches and predictions for the present and the future.

Finally, despite a welter of magazine and newspaper articles, radio and television shows, and paperback and hardcover books, the general public still appears to be appallingly misinformed regarding drugs, their abuse, the nature of their users and the genesis of the problem. For these reasons I have undertaken the task of writing this book, with the hope that it will be simultaneously factual, readable and concise.

In addition to factual data, I have included a great

many of my own interpretations and opinions. These are based on a deep and continuous commitment to, and involvement with, the problem of drug abuse over the last several years, a fact that will, I hope, mitigate any note of personal bias.

CHAPTER ONE

DRUG ABUSE—HOW EXTENSIVE IS IT?

Man's pharmacological cornucopia has provided us with a fantastic array of drugs, all of which are subject to either indiscriminate or illicit use. Indiscriminate use of drugs is practiced widely by both physicians and the general public. For example, a physician who, without adequate study, administers penicillin merely because a patient has a fever or an upper respiratory infection would have a hard time justifying such therapy to his skeptical peers. It would be pointed out to him that the statistical chances were overwhelming that the patient was infected by a virus or had some other entity which would under no conditions respond to penicillin. The physician might be giving the drug because of inadequate information about the patient, out of ignorance, or because of persistent pressures by the patient, or the patient's relatives. Although excessive prescribing by doctors of potent drugs which are potentially harmful is frequently understandable, such drug use must be considered indiscriminate and lamentable.

But over-prescribing by physicians is minuscule in comparison to the enormous amount of indiscriminate self-medication practiced by the American public. This has been precisely documented in a recent study carried out by the Stanford Research Institute. The Institute studied 86 households in California, and found a total of 2,539 medications: an average of approximately 30 medications per household. Of these 2,539 drugs, only

445, approximately 1 in 5, were prescription drugs given under medical aegis. The rest, 4 out of 5, were purchased over the counter without a prescription for purposes of self-medication, clearly illustrating the fact that the general public, not the medical profession, is to blame for the majority of indiscriminate drug use.

In this book I am, of course, primarily concerned not with the legitimately obtained drugs taken or prescribed unwisely, but rather with those drugs which are used illicitly. The drugs which are bought and sold on the black market can readily be divided into three major categories: opiates, hallucinogens, and sedatives or stimulants. To serve as an introduction and orientation for subsequent chapters, the following is a summary of some of the more important data concerning these drugs.

Opiates are narcotics. The word narcotic derives from the Greek and means benumbing. Any drug which produces sleep or stupor and at the same time relieves pain can be considered a narcotic. Medically the term is usually used in its narrow sense to refer to drugs directly derived from the opium poppy or chemically related synthetic equivalents. Ludicrously, one of the major stumbling blocks to a rational approach to our dangerous drugs has been our inability to clear up the confusion and inaccuracy which surround the use of this word. Federal narcotic control laws lump together cocaine, a stimulant; heroin, which is medically a true narcotic, and marihuana, which can be classed either as a euphoriant or hallucinogen. Many of the states have compounded the error by including under their narcotic laws barbiturate sedatives, amphetamine stimulants and potent hallucinogens such as LSD.

Thus the legal definition of a narcotic is not consistent with the medical definition, and even the medical definition may require the further clarification of specifying the drugs included under the term. Not surprisingly, the worst offenders among those promoting confusion are the newspapers and magazines which engage in yellow journalism. Presumably to sensationalize stories, they refer to all drugs used illicitly as "dope," a term of opprobrium covering stimulants, sedatives, tranquilizers, opiates, hallucinogens and a variety of other substances. Surely this overworked slang term should be dropped from our lexicon.

In this book the term narcotic shall refer specifically and only to opiate narcotics or their synthetic equivalents. These would include opium, morphine, heroin, dihydromorphinone (Dilaudid), merperidine (Demerol), methadone (Dolophine) and codeine.

There has been an enormous amount of debate concerning the number of illicit users of narcotics in the United States. By and large these polemics are unrewarding, unrevealing and unnecessary. Between 1900 and 1920 the number of narcotic addicts in the United States was clearly greater than it is now. The commonly used figure records that 1 in 400 persons in this country was addicted then as contrasted to a current incidence of between 1 in 2,000 and 1 in 4,000. However, a meaningful comparison between the first two decades of the twentieth century and the most recent twenty-year period is virtually impossible. Those addicted in the early 1900s used opium and morphine preparations, many of them freely available in commonly used patent medicines. Heroin, which had been synthesized just before the turn of the century, was no problem at all. The famed Harrison Act of 1914 attempted to control the supply and thus to reduce the availability of these drugs.

This legislation resulted in a striking decline in the prevalence of narcotic addiction in the United States, which fell to its lowest point during the war years, 1940-1945, when because of profoundly restricted supply, the number of known addicts dropped to approx-

imately 20,000. (It should be noted that all specific
figures are derived from information supplied by the
Federal Bureau of Narcotics and may suffer from substantial statistical inaccuracy because of inadequate reporting to the Bureau of individual cases of addiction.)

After World War II, heroin again flowed more freely
to the United States, and the number of addicts rose to
approximately 60,000 in the early 1950s. The figure
for 1967 shows 62,045 active addicts, more than half
residing in New York State. More recent figures show
over 60,000 addicts in New York City alone. The
current estimate for the United States is 120,000-150,-
000. The important things to note about our heroin
problem are the following:

Narcotic addiction used to be a disease of Caucasians
and Chinese, many of them in the older age group. At
present only 30 per cent of all addicts in the United
States are Caucasian. Heroin abuse is primarily a disease of repressed minorities; 50.4 per cent of the users
are Negro, 13.6 per cent Puerto Rican and 5.4 per cent
Mexican.

Narcotic abuse increasingly involves younger persons
residing in ghetto areas of our large urban centers. Half
the known addicts are under age thirty and growing
numbers are under age twenty. In the last year there
has been a veritable epidemic of heroin abuse in those
16 years and under, and with increasing frequency
heroin is used by affluent white youngsters, both in the
major cities and in suburbia.

Finally, even increased awareness of the severity of
the heroin problem, greater efforts at rehabilitation, and
stringent laws passed in the 1950s have failed to bring
any reduction in the incidence of narcotic addiction in
the United States over the last fifteen years. The law
enforcement agencies can claim, I believe with some
justification, that were it not for their efforts, both local
and federal, were it not for stringent laws, the prevalence of narcotic abuse would be far greater. Still, there

is no cause to swell with pride. Since World War II we have seen the problem grow, then become stabilized and remain on the same level for a decade and a half. In that period, thousands of heroin users have died of respiratory arrest or lung congestion due to inadvertently injecting themselves with an overdose of heroin. Many more thousands of young women have been forced into lives of depravity and prostitution to support their habit. Tens of thousands of young persons have developed abscesses, hepatitis, endocarditis, malaria and tetanus because in injecting the heroin they used contaminated needles; and hundreds of thousands have turned to crime, stealing well over a billion dollars a year in the United States to get the money to buy heroin.

At the very top sit the Mafia overlords. They don't use the drugs themselves or dirty their hands at the street level, but they are the major importers and distributors. From the destroyed bodies and lives of their victims, they receive hundreds of millions of dollars in profits every single year. We as a nation have commiserated with the victims and railed at the criminal purveyors, but appallingly little has been done to mitigate this persistent social cancer.

Marihuana is the drug which has caught the fancy of the young and the rebellious in American society. Known since antiquity, it has been used widely in Asia and Africa both medicinally and as an intoxicant.

In recent years its medicinal utility has been supplanted and currently it is used virtually exclusively as an intoxicant, stimulant or mild hallucinogen. The drug is obtained from the ubiquitous hemp plant *cannabis sativa* (or *cannabis indica*). The generic name of its derivatives is cannabis, and the active principals appear to be several tetrahydrocannabinols which are found mainly in the flowering top of the female plant, with the strength of the cannabis preparation depending on the amount of resin. Marihuana, like kif in Morocco, bhang in India and dagga in South Africa, is a relatively weak preparation made up of a mixture of stems, leaves and tops of the hemp plant. Ganja, a preparation obtained from special plants, is several times as strong as marihuana, whereas charas, which consists of concentrated cannabis resin, is four to six times as strong and must be considered a potentially potent psychedelic agent. Hashish, a powdered and sifted form of pure resin, can be considered as identical to charas.

The prevalence of use has not been well established. A United Nations survey in 1950 estimated that 200 million persons, most of them in Asia and Africa, used one or another of the myriad of cannabis preparations. The drug was introduced into the United States in the 1920s. By the 1930s its use had increased enough so that it came to the attention of the law enforcement agencies. Abetted by lurid and usually fallacious articles in the press, enforcement officials were able to convince the Congress to include marihuana in the narcotics statutes, thus establishing between categories of drugs a legal marriage which has persisted until the present.

In the 1930s most marihuana usage was among the same persons who were using heroin and other opiates. During the 1940s and 1950s there was a gradual but persistent increase in use among college students, but in the last five years consumption by young persons has reached epidemic proportions. The figures on marihuana use are so variable that all one can do is make a reasonable estimate as to the magnitude of use. *Life* magazine in July, 1967, quotes an estimate that 10 million Americans have tried marihuana at least once. *Newsweek* three weeks later used the figure 20 million and suggested that as a reasonable guess between 300,000 and 4½ million persons smoke it regularly. *Look* magazine stated that 675 million marihuana cigarettes would be smoked in the United States in 1967, enough to give 12 million weekly users a high every Saturday night. Richard Goldstein, in an informal but relatively comprehensive survey, estimated that across the country 1 in 7 college students smoked marihuana on one or more occasions during a four-year collegiate career. J. L. Simmons and Barry Winograd, in a paperback glorifying the psychedelic cult, state that 1 million marihuana cigarettes are smoked a day in California, and that this increases approximately 5 per cent per month. Dr. Joel Fort, a nationally known expert, places the number of users at 1 million. These figures of course are only guesses and are obviously open to enormous error. After all, if one takes merely the figures from two national magazines quoted, somebody is off by 100 per cent. Attempts to buttress the guesses with statistics on marihuana arrests or the amounts of the drug seized are virtually worthless. In New York City, for example, arrests of marihuana users in the last three years have increased over 100 per cent. But simultaneously, the size and efficiency of the local narcotics squad was increased. Thus the larger number of arrests or drug seizures may indicate not only greater use but also enhanced effectiveness of the local law enforcement units. There are surprisingly few studies which attempt to assess accurately the prevalence of marihuana use in a given group and even fewer studies in which some attempt is made to distinguish between the experimenter who uses marihuana on one to five occasions and the chronic or heavy user who smokes with regularity or consumes a large number of cigarettes on any one binge. Alice Lake, in a report in *Seventeen* magazine, surveyed 1,100 girls between the ages of thirteen and twenty and found that approximately 2½ per cent had tried marihuana. Approximately 1 per cent were considered regular users.

Clearly the precise amount of use will vary enormously, depending on the location of the college and the availability of the drug. At Wesleyan University in Middletown, Connecticut, 18 per cent of the students admitted using marihuana in an anonymous questionnaire. A similar study by the Princeton University Press Club gave a figure of 15 per cent for that institution. An informal study at the University of California at Los Angeles indicated 30 per cent of the students had experience with marihuana. At Brooklyn College in New York City 1,245 students responded to a questionnaire and, of these, 78, or 6.3 per cent, admitted to the use of drugs without medical approval at some time during their undergraduate years. Most of these had used marihuana. An informal 1967 survey at the same college suggests the figure is now in the 20 per cent range. Two studies were performed at Yale during the winter of 1966-1967. In the first, 18 per cent of the students admitted using marihuana on one or more occasions, and in the second, some 20 per cent. The investigators noted that the initial introduction to marihuana appeared to be maximum in the year during which the study was being carried out, suggesting an increasing incidence of experimentation. An excellent study at California Institute of Technology in March, 1967, showed that 19.8 per cent of undergraduates and 7.8 per cent of graduate students had used marihuana at least once. From all these studies in 1966-1967 it appeared reasonable to suggest that 15 per cent of college students used marihuana on one or more occasions during their academic careers. Even this commonly accepted figure may have been substantially in error; the *Reader's Digest* recently completed a nationwide college survey and concluded that only 6 per cent of students had used the drug.

More alarming for those who felt that abuse of drugs was spreading at an appalling rate were two studies relating to the use in high schools. On Long Island, 8 per cent of the students at two Great Neck high schools acknowledged use of marihuana on at least one occasion, and in a high school in the San Francisco area the figure was 20 per cent. Granting that these two areas are the ones in which illicit use of marihuana is likely to be greatest, the results were nevertheless disturbing. In 1968-1969 a variety of studies indicated that the 15 per cent 1966-1967 estimate had about doubled. In some schools and colleges the percentage was much higher, in the 50-75 per cent range. And marihuana use is by no means confined to colleges, high schools and ghetto areas. It has invaded middle- and upper-class urban and suburban communities, as well as the Armed Forces; in Vietnam an estimated 20 per cent of the troops use the drug.

It is imperative in evaluating prevalence to analyze not only the absolute incidence of use, but also the frequency with which the drug is used. In each of several studies in which frequency of use was assessed, between 50 and 70 per cent were shown to have used marihuana on no more than five occasions. Thus, despite the evidence of rapidly increasing use of marihuana, in the majority of cases this is strictly confined to transient experimentation. Of the remaining 30 to 50 per cent about half have used the drug up to a dozen times and the rest more than that.

Lysergic acid diethylamide, synthesized in 1938 and found to be a potent hallucinogen in 1943, is now felt to be the most potent mind altering drug in common use. Used primarily by medical researchers, chemists, physiologists and psychologists in the 1950s, it has become the lurid nightmare drug of the 1960s. Attempts to assess the extent of its use have been clouded by deliberate or inadvertent misstatements by its proponents. My own feeling is that its supporters have attempted to create a bandwagon philosophy, trying to convince potential recruits that everyone is using it, that it must, therefore, be relatively safe and that they, the uninitiated, should quickly join the growing coterie of those granted ecstasy, insight and visions of ineffable beauty by this most magnificent of all drugs. Whether the drug actually has any of the properties claimed by its adherents will be discussed subsequently, but it is clear there has been an obvious misrepresentation regarding the prevalence of use.

Thus, for example, *Life* magazine in March, 1966 made the dogmatic and surely undocumented statement that at least 1 million *doses* of LSD would be taken in the United States during that year. This figure has been further augmented by some of the proponents of LSD who, quoting *Life*, have said that over 1 million *persons* would use LSD during that year.

Some of the other misrepresentations by LSD adherents are far more disturbing. For example, in one of the best known interviews on the drug, which appeared in *Playboy* in September, 1966, Dr. Timothy Leary, the acknowledged high priest of the psychedelic cult, stated that "over 15 per cent of college students are currently using LSD." Subsequently Dr. Leary has admitted that the article was in error and that in point of fact he meant all hallucinogenic drugs, including marihuana and LSD. This is not the only time Dr. Leary has admixed marihuana and LSD. On May 13, 1966, in testimony before a Senate committee investigation on LSD, Dr. Leary, quoting an article in *The New Republic*, noted that 40 per cent of the students at Stanford University had been taking hallucinogens. The impression was given that the 40 per cent referred to LSD but the article quoted, included both marihuana and LSD in the hallucinogen category. Later that day when asked about the extent of LSD usage in the United States, Leary stated that approximately one-third of the college students were using hallucinogenic drugs; again he deliberately connected LSD and marihuana. A reporter for the *New York Daily News* further confused the situation by writing that Leary gave statistics used before that 1 out of every 3 college students may be experimenting with LSD and that the figures on some campuses may be as high as 65 per cent.

What are the known figures on actual use of LSD? Several figures are available from 1966-1967. At Wesleyan University, in Connecticut, 7 per cent of the students either experimented with the drug or were frequent users. The estimate at Princeton was 1 per cent to 3 per cent; at Yale it was 2 per cent; at Brooklyn College under 1 per cent; in the *Seventeen* magazine study approximately 1 per cent. At Great Neck high school a survey showed a surprisingly high 2 per cent had used LSD or other potent hallucinogens. In California some estimates in certain of the colleges ran from 10 per cent to 15 per cent; the most precise figures, those from California Institute of Technology, placed the figure at 9.2 per cent. In the informal UCLA study the estimate was 7 per cent. Recognizing that these figures are from the areas of greatest prevalence, a reasonable guess for 1966-1967 would be that, countrywide, in the range of .5 per cent to 2 per cent of college students had used LSD or a similar potent hallucinogen such as dimethyltryptamine (DMT), psilocybin or mescaline. As there are some 6 million students in college, this percentage would mean that some 30,000 to 120,000 of them have had experience with LSD or similar drugs during their college careers. The illicit and promiscuous use of this drug reached a plateau in 1968 and has not increased since, although its use has not yet declined. LSD use is not growing, but the use of other powerful hallucinogens and stimulants is.

During the period in which the LSD movement has lost momentum, no increase in abuse of sedatives or tranquilizers has been observed but there has been a modest increase in abuse of other potent hallucinogens such as mescaline, psilocybin and dimethyltryptamine and a profound increase in illicit use of stimulants of the amphetamine variety.

The number of illicit users of amphetamines is not known but surely is in the millions. Most take various stimulant pills (dexedrine, amphetamine sulfate and Methedrine being the favorites) but increasingly, young persons are turning to intravenously injected metham-phetamine (Methedrine).

Part of the stimulant boom can be explained by the enormous profits which can be realized. The mark-up from illicit chemist to street seller is 200-400-fold. Although there is little evidence of Mafia-type control of the manufacture and distribution of injectable Methedrine, the profits are so fantastic that the overlords of organized crime must be sorely tempted to get involved.

In summary then, heroin and other narcotics are used primarily in blighted areas of our large urban centers by impoverished individuals attempting to escape a depressing environment. Heroin use has increased markedly in the last year, especially in more affluent communities. The use of marihuana has increased remarkably among young people; at present approximately 30 per cent of our college population is involved and the number grows every month. Perhaps the most alarming aspect of the American drug scene is the recent increase in use of hallucinogens, marihuana, stimulants, tranquillizers, sedatives and even heroin in junior high, and sometimes in elementary, schools.

CHAPTER TWO

BEHIND THE SCENE

Why? This is the question educators, administrators, the clergy, physicians, sociologists, psychologists and parents ask themselves over and over again. Why in the 1960s should so many young people be turning to drugs?

In general the explanations proffered by those committed to repeated drug use combine facile rationalizations, obvious superficialities, sweeping generalizations and bitter statements castigating our materialistic dehumanizing society. Beneath the angry façade, there are a considerable number of separate factors which play an important role in the genesis of an individual's use of hallucinogens, opiates and stimulants. Rarely is any one factor *the* cause; rather, two or more acting in concert propel the individual into drug abuse.

Except for Kuwait, with its extraordinary oil wealth and small population, materially we are the richest country in the world. The United States accounts for only 6 per cent of the world's population but is estimated to have 50 per cent of its wealth. Our gross national product has risen from 104 billion dollars in 1929 to 714 billion dollars in 1966. In this country we spend approximately 400 billion dollars on personal goods and services every year, approximately 100 billion dollars of which goes for food, tobacco and alcohol. 25 billion dollars is spent each year on vacations. This country owns 29 per cent of the world's railroad mileage, 56 per cent of its automobiles, 40 per cent of its trucks, 43 per cent of its radios, 34 per cent of its electric power and 27 per cent of its steel. There is no need to belabor the point further. We are an extraordinarily wealthy country and this means, of course, that people can afford to pay for drugs both licit and illicit. Even in the poverty-stricken neighborhoods where heroin is most used, a surprisingly large number can pay for it out of their own earnings or from monies given to them by relatives or friends.

It is our wealth, too, that has allowed us to become a nation of pill-taking hypochondriacs. The seeds of drug abuse are to be found in the American home. Our legal ingestion of sedatives, tranquilizers and stimulants is phenomenally high; 14 to 18 per cent of all drug prescriptions written by doctors are for some form of sedative or tranquilizer. As indicated earlier, the average family medicine cabinet contains almost 30 drug items. We assume that for every valid or imaginary ill there is some magical medicament. If we feel depressed we have to have a stimulant; if we feel a little bit agitated we have to have a sedative or tranquilizer. We expect that we can reduce merely by taking pills, substituting these for old-fashioned willpower. This nation has become so medicine-oriented that patients demand antibiotics of physicians for the treatment of virus infections even though such infections are unaffected by antibiotics. Healthy people receiving the maximum requirement in vitamins take supplemental vitamin pills to keep them healthy. The amount of vitamin B-12 administered in situations in which it couldn't possibly do any good is absolutely horrendous. It's easy to blame the physician or the pharmaceutical firm and to claim that doctors are over-prescribing, but the fact of the matter is that patients are over-demanding. We as a nation refuse to recognize that mental and physical health and well-being do not necessarily come in a bottle or syringe. If young persons see their parents egregiously misusing and overusing drugs is it any wonder that they should become part of the youthful drug cult? Indeed the drug-taking proclivities of parents have been immortalized, if that is the word, in a record called "Mother's Little Helpers."

If our adult population would abjure reacting to every physical and mental stress with a pill, capsule or needle, then our young people would be far better insulated against the blandishments of the drug proponents.

It is our wealth, again, that has allowed us to become to such a large extent a sensate society. A sensate society, defined most eloquently by Pitirim Sorokin in his incisive treatise *The Crisis of Our Age,* written in 1941, is oriented to the concept that the only true reality and value is sensory. That which has reality and value must be heard, smelled, touched, tasted or otherwise physically perceived. The ineluctable consequences of this philosophy are the ascendancy of hedonism and of selfish materialism, the here and now predominating over goal-directed behavior or deferred gratification. This in itself creates problems. Sir Thomas Brown noted, "The race of delight is short." To maintain the pleasure principle, one thrill must replace another in unceasing succession. In a society in which the acquisition of wealth and power are far more important than the means by which these are achieved, in a culture for which sensory and physical pleasures are more important than ideals or constructive activity, it is inevitable that where drugs become freely available they will form an intrinsic part of the search for kicks, or as it is more euphemistically entitled, the cult of experience. Heroin gives a feeling of pleasurable lassitude and relaxation. Cocaine causes a genital rush, described by some as similar to an orgasm. Tranquilizers and sedatives frequently produce a feeling of calm and serenity. Amphetamines increase awareness of a variety of individual physical sensations, and LSD sunders the normal barriers to simultaneous perception permitting the mind to be bombarded with sensory stimuli. Indeed the enormous sensory input and the kaleidoscopic nature of the ephemeral perceptions make the hallucinogen experience induced by LSD and similar drugs the physiological apogee of the sensate ethic.

In the ghettos of this country the drugs are used not simply for kicks but as an escape from a blighted reality. During a welfare department strike a few years ago, I had occasion to help in the delivery of welfare checks to those who for one reason or another weren't able to come to the centers themselves. This gave me an opportunity to see Harlem from the inside. After just a few days of traipsing through the filth and decay, through decrepit buildings infested with cockroaches and rats, I found myself more impressed that so many people in this environment appear to resist drugs than by the fact that large numbers do turn to them.

An investigation in these ghetto areas in New York City published in October, 1966, revealed these distressing statistics:

Two families out of five have an average annual income of less than $3,000.

Nearly 25 per cent of the civilian labor force is unemployed.

A large percentage of the population lives in tenements badly in need of rehabilitation, with over one-third in such disrepair that replacement is mandatory.

Other figures for 1967, issued by the United States Labor Department, are equally discouraging. The unemployment rate in the United States averaged 3.7 per cent. In the poverty areas of eight large cities, it ranged from 8.1 per cent to 13.2 per cent. If, to the regularly listed unemployed, one adds the jobless who have dropped out of the labor market, and those who are in low paying part-time jobs, then the so-called sub-employment rate for the poverty areas of these eight urban centers ranges from 24.6 per cent to 45.3 per cent. In these areas there is always relentless poverty, under-education, inadequate and dilapidated housing, lack of job opportunity, extraordinarily high rates of disease, disrupted family units and welfare dependency. As of 1967, approximately 6 out of every 10 Negro youths reaching age eighteen in these areas had at some time or other been supported by welfare aid to dependent children. The data for 1968 and 1969 are virtually identical to those recorded for 1967.

Both in the ghettos and in the affluent suburban communities of this country, the deterioration of the family may explain many of the ills of our society. For here, perhaps, is the primary American tragedy of the twentieth century.

The divorce rate in our society has increased progressively over the last three decades until at present there are approximately 500,000 divorces every single year. One out of every four marriages ends either in divorce or annulment, and to this, one must add the substantial number in which family breakup is not formalized by either divorce or annulment procedures.

The problem is not likely to abate. Young married couples are entirely aware that if reality does not live up to expectation it is easy to break up a marriage and start over again. The family has also increasingly abrogated its educational responsibilities. During the nineteenth century, the family was responsible for an extraordinarily large portion of the children's education. Today's familial abjuration of educational obligations might have been tolerable if the schools had adequately replaced parental educational functions. But this has not happened. Indeed, in our public schools in urban centers, discipline is often so lax that effective education is becoming almost impossible. Although some individual teachers serve in an effective avuncular role, many others do not, and in any case the influence of the teacher is no substitute for the influence of the parent. Even if the school and the teachers can maintain disci-

pline and can effect the education for which the parents
have relinquished responsibility, those children who
grow up in broken or unhappy homes are at great
disadvantage. They have no pride in their family to fall
back on, no parental unit to advise and support them
and, equally important, no established parental guidelines, so that the boundaries between right and wrong,
between wants and needs, are blurred, making them
more susceptible to the blandishments of the drug cult.
When a user or proselytizer of drugs urges them to try
marihuana or LSD, they are less likely to feel that they
should refuse because their parents would not approve.
There can be no other influence as important in the
development of an individual as the family unit; yet we
as a society, with an insouciance that is absolutely
appalling, are allowing that unit to continue its progressive deterioration.

Nowhere, of course, is the family unit more profoundly sundered than in the ghetto areas of the larger
urban centers, a situation that was brilliantly and in-
cisively catalogued by Nathan Glazer and Daniel
Moynihan in their monograph entitled, "Beyond the
Melting Pot." The data are truly astounding. A 1960
survey of 353,000 Negro families in the New York
metropolitan area showed that one-quarter were headed
by women, as contrasted to less than one-tenth of white
households. The rate of illegitimacy among Negroes is
estimated at fourteen to fifteen times that among
whites. In a more recent article Moynihan states that
probably not more than a third of the children of
low-income Negro families reach the age of eighteen
having lived all their lives with both their parents.

The data of Isidor Chein and his colleagues, detailed
in their book, *The Road to H*, bear equally cogently on
the relationship between family problems and drug
abuse. In deprived areas they found that among young
heroin users there was a disturbed relationship between
parents, as evidenced by separation, divorce, open hos-

tility, lack of warmth or lack of mutual interest, in 97
per cent of the cases. Almost always, as far as the child
was concerned, the focus of these difficulties was the
loss of the father figure. In 80 per cent of cases the boy
experienced an extremely weak father-son relationship;
in 48 per cent the boy did not have a father figure at
all during a significant part of childhood; the father
figure was cool or hostile in 52 per cent; the father
figure was an immoral model in 23 per cent; the mother
figure was more important than the father in the boy's
life during late childhood in 73 per cent; the parental
standards for the boy were vague or inconsistent in 63
per cent; and in 23 per cent there was no clear pattern
of parental roles in the formation of disciplinary policy.
It is important to note that in these studies family chaos
was found equally among heroin users who were native
white, Negro or Puerto Rican, indicating that among
those who turn to heroin, family breakdown is not
indigenous to any one specific ethnic group.

In conjunction with the deterioration of the family
unit, American society since World War II has become
extraordinarily permissive. This is true not only at a
family level but also in many of our educational institutions. A variety of studies suggests that parents have
interpreted the word progressive to be synonymous with
lack of guidelines or discipline. In other instances the
family unit is so chaotic that permissiveness is virtually
mandatory. The result is that young people, especially
in middle- and upper-income groups, are reaching college age without any firmly established behavioral concepts about the dividing line between propriety and
impropriety. As a result, the individual reacts to a
variety of situations, including the possibility of drug
use, on the basis of emotions and wants rather than
within the context of parentally established and accepted guidelines. The permissive philosophy when
viewed as a positive approach, rather than the inevitable consequences of familial deterioration, makes the

assumption that the young person, given clear alternatives, is capable of making a mature decision. The crucial question, of course, is whether young people between the ages of fifteen and twenty really do have the maturity to develop optimally in an inordinately permissive environment. There is no facile answer to this question, but logic dictates that a certain percentage of young people will thrive in such a milieu, while others, functioning aimlessly, will be susceptible to a variety of potentially inimical influences, including drugs.

In our colleges four factors appear to be acting in concert to promote permissiveness. First, there is the valid realization that many students can handle themselves maturely in a relaxed environment. Second, in some colleges there are suprising parental pressures on the college administration not to be particularly rigorous in enforcing disciplinary measures. Third, we are undergoing a profound liberalization of sexual codes in our society and it is inevitable that the relaxation of the disciplinary rules regarding sexual behavior will spill over into other areas. Fourth, the shibboleth of the generation gap has mesmerized and disturbed many college administrators, leading them to believe it is more important for students to love them than to respect them.

These four factors, acting in unison, have resulted not only in relaxation of what were undoubtedly excessively rigorous restrictions, but have also had some undesirable side effects from the point of view of drug use. For the most part, rightly or wrongly, students have always regarded modification of the disciplinary rules as a victory for them over authority, and the derivative assumption has been that if they are given more latitude in one area of behavior they are in essence being given more latitude in every area of behavior. Thus the changes in the regulations may apply to the presence of members of the other sex in the dormitory, late hours, social events, exam-taking, time away from campus, or political activities on campus, but frequently the students assume that the permissiveness also pertains to drug use.

This situation never applies to heroin and infrequently to LSD, but it does to marihuana. The administration having decided that the students are to be treated as mature individuals, and that the guidelines relating to a variety of behavioral patterns shall be intentionally lax, are in essence sold the same position concerning marihuana use by the student body, or, in point of fact, by what usually amounts to a small group of marihuana activists.

At one large Eastern university, disciplinary actions are initially heard before a special student unit. Encouraged by a tolerant administration, the students have adopted a code holding that sexual activity held behind closed doors is only the business of the people directly involved. On the same campus there has been a growing demand that the administration not only ignore this form of activity, but also that related to drugs so long as the drugs are consumed in the privacy of the students' rooms. A substantial portion of the faculty has been openly sympathetic to this point of view.

A Midwestern college administration was quoted recently in a national magazine as stating that if an individual were caught smoking marihuana, the student would not be turned over to any law enforcement agency and, more important, that no disciplinary actions would be taken against the student within the college. When permissiveness goes that far, when the imprimatur of the educational institution is placed on drug use, then an increase in abuse of drugs in our colleges is inevitable.

But the problems do not lie solely in disintegrating family units or permissive educators and parents. Especially over the last few years we have become more and more a rudderless society. The leadership of this country at municipal, state and national levels is clearly dominated by men of limited ability and restricted imagination, who lack the capacity to sustain an aura of vigor or of important accomplishment. This is not intended to be an indictment of any given individual, any party, or of all persons in the upper echelons of government. There are many who are capable and energetic, bright, and constructive. But the overall image presented by both major political parties is an unfortunate combination of anachronisms, ineptitude, mediocrity, self-interest and, worst of all, an inability to deal with the major problems of our times. One can dispute this interpretation, but not the fact that it is largely believed by our young people. Two derivative consequences of inadequate leadership are non-commitment and a growing disrespect for laws.

Drug abuse is in part a disease of the uncommitted. The so-called hippies (the flower people) fully recognize, indeed talk interminably about, the important problems in our society, such as slums, international aggression, the civil rights movement, etc., but they determinedly remain aloof from commitment to these problems. It is among these inward-oriented groups that drug abuse flourishes.

In part the disrespect for the law by the young merely reflects the behavior patterns of their elders. Across the country over and over again there is incontrovertible evidence of chicanery, venality and dishonesty by public officials who either have their hand in the public till or use their position for personal financial gain. Children listen to their parents gleefully recount how they cheated the government on their income tax, undermined a business rival through techniques of dubious morality, or escaped traffic fines by outrageous prevarications. These examples could of course be multiplied many fold. Yet that same older generation in some strange fashion thinks it has the right to ask younger people to obey certain of the laws of the land, ones that the older generation happens to think are worth obeying.

What is a young person expected to think when he hears of a California elementary school principal who voluntarily and publicly states she has used marihuana for eighteen years and found it beneficial. If an educator must break the drug laws, surely common sense dictates it should be done covertly and in private, not advertised in the national press. At issue in this particular case was not so much marihuana use per se, but rather the violation of established laws. The principal was subsequently dismissed from her job, a punishment clearly merited for her outrageous irresponsibility in setting an example for her students of willful disobedience of the laws.

If parents, educators, writers, artists, social and religious groups ignore laws which displease them, why should young people feel any compulsion to obey laws they don't like, including those which relate to marihuana and LSD. As LaRochefoucauld said, "Nothing is so infectious as example, and we never do great good or evil without producing the like."

There is no clear evidence that reaction to the war in Vietnam directly results in drug abuse. However there is a growing body of medical opinion led by Charles Clay Dahlberg, a well-known New York psychiatrist, which holds that reactive depression is important. A variety of factors including social pressures, family discord or anxieties over studies, employment or impending military service may result in depression which actively propels the individual to illicit or indiscriminate drug use.

In some young persons, and often those of greater sensitivity, the negative reaction to the milieu in which they find themselves is more severe and results in a psychosocial behavior pattern often referred to by the term alienation.

According to the Oxford International Dictionary,

alienation is defined as the state of estrangement; in this
case the estrangement is from the values of society and
family. As the concept applies to drug abuse, there are
two major alienated groups. The first, comprised primarily of Negroes, Mexicans and Puerto Ricans, resides
in our urban ghettos; the second consists of more
affluent young persons. In blighted areas behavioral
extremes engendered by estrangement result in a variety
of antisocial activities, from violent rebellion on the one
hand to withdrawal through drug use on the other. Far
different is the alienation of the relatively affluent college student. Constituting at most 5 per cent and probably nearer 1 per cent of the college population, and a
greater percentage of college dropouts, this group's approach to life and society can best be characterized as
mordant and cynical.

For the alienated, American society is ugly, tawdry,
sordid and reprehensibly materialistic. Its values are
considered dishonest, hypocritical, constricting and dehumanizing. The alienated make a fetish of immediacy,
spontaneity and genuineness and trumpet their complete repudiation of anything which to them smacks of
materialism, phoniness, self-deception or premeditation.
Life is unhappy, lonely, meaningless and boring. They
reject with disdain their families, the teaching establishment and virtually every facet of our society. They are
detached from their colleagues and even from themselves. The two men who have studied the alienation
syndrome most extensively and expound upon it most
articulately are Seymour Halleck, director of student
psychiatry at the University of Wisconsin, and Kenneth
Keniston of Yale University, whose treatise entitled
"The Uncommitted: Alienated Youth in American Society" is considered the most important exposition of the
problem.

Halleck characterizes the alienated college student from a behavioral standpoint as follows:

First, such students have a tendency to live in the present and to avoid commitment to people, causes or ideas. All gratification is immediate, the future is felt to hold nothing and reaching the age of thirty is considered synonymous with emotional and experiential death. The alienated student is totally unable to seriously commit himself to anything. He may have periods in which he becomes extraordinarily interested in a cause or idea and may throw himself into it with prodigious enthusiasm, devoting large amounts of time to it, but he is incapable of sustaining this interest.

Second, there is an almost total lack of communication with parents or other adults. This is the generation-gap syndrome carried to the extreme. Third, the alienated have an ill-defined concept of self (as is beautifully documented by Keniston). The alienated individual suffers from such perpetual inner turmoil that it results in his continually asking but never answering such questions as who he is, where he is going, what the meaning of his life is and what his role in society should be. His is the constant search for identity, a quest that is almost uniformly unsatisfying and unrewarding because his anxieties prevent his going about it in meaningful or constructive fashion.

Fourth, there is a tendency toward sudden severe depression, which may, of course, lead to attempts of suicide. Fifth, there is an inability to concentrate or to study. Sixth, sexual behavior is promiscuous but ungratifying. Although the alienated are among the most consistent and enthusiastic boosters of diverse and unlimited sexual experiences, their own promiscuous behavior is, in Halleck's experience, often described as unsatisfying and meaningless. The women may not experience orgasm, and the men often complain of impotence, premature ejaculation and inability to ejaculate.

011 52

Thus the alienated student hates society, rejects his family, distrusts everyone, and, torn by anxieties, a chronic identity crisis, and an inability to respect himself, he is incapable of giving or accepting love. Uncertain of who he is, convinced life is meaningless, unable to participate in goal-directed activity, he is a lost soul wandering from sensate experience to sensate experience. He frequently reports these experiences with enormous enthusiasm, but in reality they are no more meaningful to him than the rest of his empty life, and consequently he attempts in some way to enhance them, beautify them, or invest them with some sort of meaning. His use of drugs such as LSD is an attempt to do just that, as well as to show his utter disdain for the regulations of society. Today he is often to be found among the hippies, ostensibly having a wonderful time doing his thing. But for the alienated it is all façade. No cult of experience, no drug, no fad is likely to change his pervasive pessimism and unhappiness.

The alienated young person is obviously especially susceptible to the blandishments of the drug cult, but there is an almost equal danger for the young person who is excessively influenced by the actions and opinions of his peer group. In fact, among the large number of factors that influence an individual's decision whether or not to use drugs, there is none quite so insidious as the drug-using peer group. The domination of the peer group is found equally on the littered and fetid streets of urban slums and on charming, bucolic college campuses. The old concept of the venal purveyor of drugs waiting outside the school yard to entice some unsuspecting youngster into the ravages of drug abuse is today (and has been for quite some time) a totally anachronistic concept. In the slums of Harlem where heroin use abounds, it is the drug user who makes other drug users. In *The Road to H*, Chein and his associates describe from interviews with youthful addicts the initiation into the world of heroin. In the following descriptions taken from that book, caps and pills, bag and deck refer to heroin. Snorting or sniffing is taking the drug nasally. Skin-popping refers to injecting the heroin under the skin, and main-lining to injecting it directly into the vein.

"It was raining and I was tired. I was standing in a doorway when this friend of mine came by. He said want a pickup. I said sure, so we popped."

"I was at a party, everybody was having a good time. I wanted to be one of the crowd. I thought if it didn't hurt them it wouldn't hurt me. That started the ball rolling. They were sniffing it at that time. Two or three pulled out a few caps and said, 'Here if you want to try.' I accepted. They weren't trying to addict me, they just gave it to me."

"It was in school. At that time all the boys were using it. A friend offered me some. Said it was something different. He had just started using it himself and he wanted me to try."

"One of the seamen I knew—knew I smoked reefers (marihuana) and thought I ought to try heroin sometime. Hanging around the block there were a couple of fellows who were new around the block. They were going down to the cellar to snort the stuff. They asked me to join them. I was a little leery at first but then I went with them. They offered me a little and I snorted it."

"Some of us was in a car. We were going to town one night so one of the guys says let's take off (use drugs). I said not me I don't want any but one of the guys owed me $2 so he said 'Come on I'll give you four pills and we'll call it even.' So I tried. That was just skin-popping. The next day I was with this same guy and he was *main-lining*—wanted me to try it. I tried two pills at once that time."

"I was going downtown with a guy—he wanted to borrow $1.25. He went and got a bag or a deck. It was nice stuff—would have cost anybody else twelve dollars. He asked if I wanted some—I said no, but being as I had put some money into it I changed my mind and sniffed some."

"A bunch of fellows my age were going down on the corner. Someone said 'let's try some.' No one knew where to buy it then but we made a contact. We went up on the roof and snorted."

The neophyte succumbs to the urgings of his peers for a variety of reasons. These include curiosity, a fear of being called afraid or square, being anxious to keep up with friends, or merely a somewhat insouciant willingness to go along with what everyone else is doing.

Drug-taking, especially of heroin, is usually a communal affair, at least in the early stages of an individual's experience. Indeed the main reason for the extraordinarily high incidence among heroin users of hepatitis (a frequently severe, chronic or even lethal infectious disease of the liver), is the practice of sharing unsterilized needles. These needles, contaminated by the hepatitis virus, are passed from individual to individual either with no attempt at sterilization or with egregiously ineffective ones. Interestingly, the heroin users are perfectly well aware of the dangers of hepatitis incurred by this type of unsterile communal use of needles.

Peer-group usage is also influential in use of both marihuana and LSD. Characteristically, young persons are introduced to marihuana by their friends, at school, at dances, at parties or other social events. Once again it is worth stressing that it is not the venal Cosa Nostra pusher who initiates the young person to marihuana use but rather the youth's own contemporaries. If an individual attends a college at which 20 per cent to 40 per cent of the students have experimented with marihuana, if marihuana is readily available and his friends use marihuana, it is very likely that a combination of curiosity and peer-group influence will lead him to experiment too. Indeed, at an age at which the approbation of one's colleagues is of immense importance to a maturing but emotionally insecure individual, it takes great strength of character to reject use if a substantial percentage of the peer group is involved.

With marihuana, there is an additional aspect to peer-group use; among college and high school students those selling the drug tend to be either members of, or on the fringe of, the peer group. (Here, I am using the term peer group to refer not to a small circle of an individual's friends but rather the college group as a whole.) The revolt of young people against the marihuana statutes is so extensive that there is little if any opprobium attached to selling small amounts of the drug. This means of course that the marihuana purveyor is not a pariah but instead is an accepted member of the peer group. The drug is thus very easy to obtain, and once an individual is initiated into its use, continued acquisition of the drug requires virtually no effort.

LSD too is promulgated by the peer group. The drug is purchased by college students, smuggled by college students and sold within the campuses by college students; its main adherents and proselytizers can be found among the peer group on any college campus at which its use is prevalent.

There are other pressures on young persons which can, more indirectly, turn some of them toward drugs. Perhaps most important are the fear of an inability to compete and sexual insecurity. In the ghetto a young man knows that he may not even be permitted to compete, but in our colleges (and this is now filtering down to the high schools) there is increasing fear of an innate inability to compete. Kenneth Keniston has called this the pressure of cognitive professionalism.

Since World War II, the demands upon our student population have grown enormously both in quality and quantity. These demands begin in high school with the increasing competition for college positions. To quote Keniston, "What matters increasingly to admissions committees and college graders is the kind of highly intellectual, abstracting, reasoning ability that enables the student to do well on college boards, graduate records and other admission tests and once he is in college or graduate school to turn out consistently high grades that will enable him to overcome the next academic hurdle." Students today work harder than ever before to achieve the type of intellectual and academic excellence which will permit them to compete in an increasingly scientific and technological world. The majority of course adjust in one way or another to the demands and either enter an area in which the new technology predominates, or, abjuring it, turn to business, law, teaching or the arts. For many students the pressures of the academic schedule may be rigorous and painful, but they are able to adapt to it with various degrees of enthusiasm. For some, however, the increasing demands for academic excellence are greeted with misgivings and apprehension. Some, despite these apprehensions, continue in academic grace and even thrive. Others, in one way or another, withdraw; one of the mechanisms of withdrawal is increasing use of, and dependence on, a variety of drugs including amphetamines, barbiturates, marihuana or LSD.

During the last decade our conventions regarding sexual behavior have changed so greatly that premarital intercourse and promiscuity are no longer considered inappropriate, stigma being attached only to pregnancy out of wedlock, a likelihood now largely obviated by the availability of contraceptive pills. It used to be that a male could express his virility by going out with girls and engaging in various petting activities ranging from kissing to digital genital manipulation. Many normal, heterosexual, virile young men were therefore not faced with the ultimate test of their manhood, the ability to perform adequately in bed. It is abundantly clear that a substantial proportion of young men suffer from sexual insecurity or from premature ejaculation, or are in some other way incapable in their own eyes of performing optimally in sexual intercourse. There is nothing abnormal about this; the overwhelming majority of these individuals become perfectly adequate or even unusually good lovers in the course of prolonged courtship with a single girl or after marriage. Until the last decade they had been protected from facing their own sexual insecurities because it was considered to be an adequate manifestation of virility to engage in various types of sexual play without actually consummating intercourse. Stringent dormitory rules frequently compelled the action to take place in the back seat of a car or in other sub-optimal physical circumstances, allowing rationalizations for sex play without intercourse, such as: "she was too nice a girl," "the quarters were too cramped," "she wouldn't let me go any further," etc. But whatever the particular type of rationalization, the young man was protected from exposure to his own insecurities and potential inadequacies. Now this is no longer so. The miniskirt revolution is upon us. To quote one Tuli Kupferberg in the *Berkeley Barb*: "See the miniskirts. See the beautiful legs. Yes, they lead to the cunt and these girls do not tease ... they fuck. Can you take it?" That's not exactly the way I would have put it but it does make a valid point.

Now, at least a fair percentage of the time, when a young man takes a girl into his room she expects to have intercourse and he knows it. The combination of increased opportunity as a result of more permissive regulations and the feeling, whether valid or not, that the girl expects him to attempt intercourse, prevents rationalization and compels many persons to face squarely up to any potential sexual insecurities. Given a little experience or a patient girl, the inadequacies and insecurities may be circumvented or overcome. Some may obviate the sexual crisis by sublimating, immersing themselves in extra-curricular activities of a nonsexual nature. But for others, in a society obsessed with sex, the fears that their virility will be denigrated or laughed at compel them to seek some sort of withdrawal from the sex game. For those who cannot or will not sublimate, the acknowledged passivity of the drug experience helps the user to avoid the potential humiliation of sexual confrontation. Alternatively, some young men, determined to document their virility by satisfactory sexual performance, will take alcohol, marihuana or stimulants in the hope of reducing their inhibitions, thus enabling them to perform more effectively. For young women, marihuana and LSD may play a role similar to that described for the male. For them, too, the slackening sexual restrictions present substantial problems. Many of them of course cope with the new challenges in straightforward and satisfactory fashion. Many adjust without engaging in sexual intercourse, at least during their college years. Others have intercourse on only a very limited basis with a single partner, and still others are able to adapt to a more promiscuous way of life with considerable equanimity. But for some, who feel that the new sexual mores demand they become experienced in sexual intercourse, but who are ambivalent for a variety of reasons, including religious background, family ties or fears of conception, drugs are a perfect out. For some, marihuana, by reducing inhibitions, can condition them to accepting sexual intercourse. On the other hand, by increasing passivity and emphasizing the drug experience, marihuana, as well as LSD, can create a situation in which sexual activity is not deemed necessary.

Of course, for many young people no complicated psychological pressures are necessary to push them toward drug use—mere curiosity is enough. An old Yiddish proverb states: "A man should live if only to satisfy his curiosity." And thus it is that many young persons, especially those in high school or college, will succumb to the not unnatural urge to investigate the effects of drugs available in their milieu. The major agents involved of course are marihuana, the more potent hallucinogens and, among high school students, the amphetamines. For the curious, the combination of profound effects and unpredictability tend in a bizarre way to attract rather than to repel. By and large the curious will be transient experimenters. They are likely to try LSD only once and marihuana on only one to five occasions. Of course, for some of them the experimentation may prove dangerous, even lethal, especially for those who try LSD. A small percentage of these dabblers will become enthralled with the drug experience, and for them it can become a way of life. Mere curiosity rarely leads to heroin use in colleges, but it does account for some initiation into the narcotic experience in high schools in blighted areas, and even more among school dropouts in urban ghettos.

It is in relation to the strength of simple curiosity that we must judge the effects of the extraordinary amount of publicity given to drugs over the past few years, particularly to the use of LSD. In the beginnings of the LSD movement, the word was spread by people who for the most part might be called genuine seekers. They constitute only a minuscule portion of the current psychedelic cult, but it was their search for truth, beauty, mystical experiences, mind expansion and creativity that gave the movement whatever initial validity it may

have possessed. For those of the seekers who found the
world sordid and tawdry but were incapable of fighting
what they considered a grotesque environment, LSD
promised peace and beauty. For those who deeply and
honestly questioned the meaning of life and their role in
the universe, LSD held out hopes of discovering some
truths about themselves, their interactions with others
and with the world, and even the meaning of life itself.
For those who felt that orthodox religion created an
artificial barrier between them and God, and who were
sympathetic to a pantheistic heterodoxy, LSD offered
the potential for a communion with God that religion
had denied them. For those who felt that the constant
bombardment of external stimuli was constricting, the
drug offered an opportunity to explore a heretofore repressed and restricted inner self. For those seekers who
felt shackled by the monotonous regularity of their
daily lives, or who as artists or writers were plagued by
fears of diminishing creativity, LSD offered rejuvena-
tion and new horizons. Aldous Huxley and Timothy
Leary were the pied pipers and they, the seekers, the
acolytes. For them the clarion call to beauty, truth,
mysticism and creativity was irresistible.

That the ancedotal accounts of LSD's putative glories were unsubstantiated meant little. For that small
number of persons in our society who are true seekers,
promise alone is enough. So off they went on their
unending search, this time with the aid of drugs. The
seekers themselves may have found little, but in the
beginnings of the LSD movement they were among the
most important proponents of the LSD experience; they
were on a valid quest, and one could challenge their
methods but not the merit of their search. Among the
current LSD and/or marihuana users, only a few
belong in this category. But there are many young
persons taking drugs for purposes of rebellion, kicks,
sex or a variety of other reasons, who, with appalling

superficiality, plagiarize and distort the philosophic views of the seekers in order to justify their own drug use.

With the impetus given by the seekers it is hardly surprising that the hallucinogenic movement got out of hand very quickly. We live in a world of mass markets and instant communication. If somebody smokes banana scrapings on the West Coast one evening, it is entirely possible that the event, labeled as the latest kick, will be reported on radio and television on the East Coast by the next evening. And it is equally possible for an enterprising psychedelic salesman to have banana posters and banana buttons on sale across the country a few weeks later. Banana scrapings may be entirely harmless, but some other new kick may be potentially dangerous and, either way, many juicy news tidbits are almost inevitably reported uncritically. It would, of course, be impossible to expect the news media to depict simultaneously both the pleasurable effects and the potential dangers of a new kick; indeed, it is likely that any possible dangers will be unknown when the use of a new drug first becomes newsworthy. There can be little doubt, however, that the lightning spread of new drug fads can be attributed in part to the rapid reporting techniques of the mass media, as well as to the possibility of making a quick profit by marketing inexpensive decorative items which glorify the drug's use.

When the LSD story first broke, I was on a television program which presented a movie lasting approximately fifteen minutes and showing an LSD session in California. The young people, who obviously knew they were on camera, were making remarks such as, "It's absolutely wonderful," "It's great," "I can't describe it," "You all ought to try it for yourself." I submit that after that kind of free advertisement, a panel such as ours, which was at least in part devoted to warning people of the dangers of the drug, could not possibly play an effective avuncular role. We could only be regarded as eminently square representatives of the establishment, who simply didn't want young people to have fun. Of course, the argument of the news media is that they cannot arbitrate but can only present the data and alternatives, permitting the viewer to make his own decisions. This is the kind of rationalization which supposedly absolves them from all responsibility. To my mind, it just doesn't.

During the early days of the LSD movement virtually all the national magazines, major newspapers, radio stations and television networks contributed to the spread of LSD usage through uncritical or even openly laudatory reporting.

A typical example of uncritical writing can be found in *Look* magazine of April 18, 1967. One of the features is a speculative article entitled "The Love Hippies," based on what appears to have been a brief walk through the Haight-Ashbury area of San Francisco. The following excerpts illustrate the tenor of the article. "Their bodies decked in 'ecstatic dress,' their vehicles painted in all the wiggly colors of the psychedelic rainbow, their minds expanded by LSD to bright visions of brotherhood, they seem to me to be America's newest revolutionaries. One girl was wearing a button that said 'I'm a hope freak.' And in a thousand words it could not have said more about the special brand of optimism they are selling—or rather giving away—in an age of despair. This is a different message and a trickier one. Freaks for hope, after all, like fools for Christ, can either move the world or fall on their faces and the margin between the two is thin. Perhaps I shouldn't even try to analyze a movement that consists mainly of other people's emotions. . . . Still there is a tantalizing idea at work here and if I might pass along my unheightened perceptions, this is what I think is going on. San Francisco's hippies want to overthrow the reign of pure reason. They feel that we have boxed ourselves into most of our present corners with verbal and logical decisions, meanwhile allowing our senses to wither and losing our capacity for wonder, love and joy. Therefore, the biggest favor that they can bestow is to turn other people on both in their everyday actions and in their arts. LSD is of course the turn-on agent. Most hippies have taken a 'trip' at least once and the majority take it with some regularity. In any case it opened a door to intense levels of awareness—'to the rhythmic beauty of detail which the drugs reveal in common things,' as one of their favorite writers, Alan W. Watts, has put it, and to 'a relationship [with each other] of the most vivid understanding, forgiveness and love. . . .' I detected a positive current in San Francisco that could turn all the rest of us on, releasing energies that we have become too cynical or too embarrassed to use. But then I've always been a hope freak myself."

This article clearly glorifies the hippie movement and has been used extensively not only as a justification for the hippie movement but as a justification for all aspects of it, including the use of LSD and other hallucinogenic drugs. One can only wonder how many young people, reading this uncritical, ecstatic and speculative statement, might have been influenced to drop out, to join the hippie movement and to expose themselves to the dangers incurred by the indiscriminate use of drugs such as LSD.

Things have changed somewhat for the better recently. In December of 1967, for instance, NBC presented a three-part report on the hippie movement. Shown on the Huntley-Brinkley evening news program, it concluded that the hippie ideals of love and peace were entirely secondary to the taking of drugs, and dramatically illustrated the dangers of drugs, from glue-sniffing to LSD, by showing the acute physical suffering of a number of young people on what even the most adamant drug user would have to call very bad trips. Thereafter, most of the television and radio reports on drug abuse have emphasized the negative aspects of the drug experience. But it will take a great deal more of such reporting to make up for the irresponsibility of the mass media in the early days of the LSD movement.

Also of importance in spreading the drug cult are the various vituperative underground newspapers devoted to protest, attacks on law enforcement agencies, and promotion of the use of psychedelic drugs, especially marihuana and LSD. The *Berkeley Barb,* the *Los Angeles Free Press,* the *East Village Other* and the *Oracle* are perhaps the best known representatives of the underground press. And while it is true that some of them have recently begun to print articles warning of the dangers of amphetamines and of chromosome damage from the use of LSD, such warnings almost invariably end with a cry for the development of a *safe* drug and urge further experimentation.

Uncritical commentary by the news media is not the only means by which hallucinogenic drugs are promoted. In addition, there are important commercial aspects to the psychedelic movement which have unquestionably focussed the attention of the American public on the use of LSD and marihuana as effectively as any national advertising campaign. Music, drama, fashion, architecture, even industry have been affected by the movement.

Discotheques have sprung up across the country which feature psychedelic movies, music, decorations and even psychedelic topless dancers or strip-teasers. In New York City, in the East Village, at The Head Shop and Psychedelicatessen one can buy virtually any psychedelic accessory imaginable. In many cities psychedelic book stores, poster shops and rug shops are sprouting. Indeed, one estimate in a Washington newspaper suggested that astute businessmen consider this to be a 25 billion-dollar-a-year market. Some of the commercial aspects of the psychedelic movement directly relate to the use of drugs—for example, the sale of pipes for smoking marihuana. But for the most part the commercial arm of the movement does not directly proselytize. Nevertheless, it is an enormously potent force in conditioning people to acceptance and use of hallucinogenic drugs. What each of these commercial enterprises is saying is "enjoy us and turn on." But implicit (and sometimes quite explicit) in this is the notion that whatever joys and pleasures you get from the psychedelic items they are selling are minuscule compared to the ineffable ecstasies and glories of the use of drugs, especially LSD and, to a secondary extent, marihuana.

The psychedelic movement has also been exploited in two recent motion pictures, "The Love Ins," a Four Leaf Production presented by Columbia Pictures, and "The Trip," and American International product. The problem is that such films not only exploit, but also advertise, the supposed glories of taking LSD. In his *New York Times* review of "The Love Ins," Bosley Crowther wrote as follows: " 'The Love Ins' might sound slightly critical of hippyism, and it is, if one only sees and listens to the mild pokes and vague suggestions of criticism it contains. But for the most part this lurid melodrama which Sam Katzman has produced and Arthur Dreifuss directed is a gaudy, gleeful glorification of the fun that hippies have at their jolly outdoor love-ins and on their phantasmagorical trips."

Finally, there are the songs. At one point in 1967, a survey of the top 40 pop records found that 16 contained a positive drug message. To any hip young person the words of Bob Dylan's song, "The Tambourine Man" ("my senses have been stripped"), are an unequivocal drug reference. Lest anyone miss the point, "smoke rings of my mind" makes it more directly.

It is, of course, almost impossible to determine to what extent such lyrics, in song after song, coupled with admitted drug-taking by such groups as the Rolling

Stones and the Beatles, really influence young people toward the taking of drugs. Some might even argue that by allowing vicarious participation in the psychedelic world, such songs act as a kind of safety valve. But it seems unarguable that such widespread references to drugs in popular music create a kind of climate of acceptance for drug use, as well as further piquing the curiosity of susceptible young people.

In the long run, of course, any drug movement is entirely predicated on easy availability. And that is where some of our greatest problems lie. Heroin is manufactured in laboratories in France or Italy and then is brought to the United States through a variety of devious routes. Despite the constant and increasing vigilance of the customs officers and the Federal Bureau of Narcotics and Dangerous Drugs, it is estimated that some 90 per cent of the heroin slips into this country undetected. Marihuana grows wild in many areas in the United States and truckloads—literally— are brought in from Mexico. Thirteen billion sedatives and tranquilizers, pills or capsules, are manufactured in this country every year; as much as 50 per cent of these are diverted into the illicit market. D-lysergic acid diethylamide can be smuggled into or manufactured within the United States. The result is that a farrago of drugs are readily available for illicit use. Walk through the streets of Harlem or the Lower East Side in New York City and you can purchase heroin with relative ease. In Greenwich Village or Harvard Square in Cambridge, Massachusetts, or on campuses in Michigan or in Berkeley, California, it's easy to procure a variety of drugs, including marihuana, LSD and stimulants.

If these drugs remain readily available for illicit use and there continues to be a large pool of susceptible individuals, then one can predict with great assurance that abuse of hallucinogens, stimulants and narcotics will persist and flourish.

CHAPTER THREE

GLUE/GAS—UP/DOWN

For the very young, turning on is frequently accomplished by inhaling a variety of solvents found in cements or glues used with polystyrene plastics, household cement, glues used in making model airplanes, fingernail polish remover, lacquer and paint thinners, lighter and cleaning fluids and gasoline. Each of these contains volatile organic substances; the cements and glues all contain toluene, sometimes combined with acetone; fingernail polish remover consists of acetone and aliphatic acetates, lighter and cleaning fluids have as a major constituent naphtha and sometimes carbon tetrachloride, and gasoline contains a variety of hydrocarbons. These are inhaled in a number of ways; gasoline is sniffed directly from the container in which it resides, whereas the other substances are either put on rags, which are then held up and sniffed, or are placed in plastic bags and the head of the bag held over the mouth and nose. For those eager to get a quicker effect, airplane glues or cement can be gently heated, causing the volatile intoxicants to produce their effects more rapidly.

After inhaling any of the volatile substances listed above for a short period of time, the user feels drunk, dizzy, and experiences substantial euphoria. Colors generally appear to be extraordinarily vivid. Not infrequently, a feeling of reckless abandon, grandiosity and personal omnipotence supervene. Hallucinations may or may not occur and may either be visual or auditory in nature. Headache frequently is noted, and the initial feelings of exhilaration may be replaced by frightening delusions and hallucinations. The following are some typical published descriptions given by individuals who had unpleasant experiences under the influence of glue or gas. "The devil was lighting fires around naked women." "Tigers and wild birds were rushing at me." "I started seeing little ants crawling all over the ground real fast." "Little men who were horrible and came out of the ground threatened me with death." Interestingly (in this case) during the early phases of gas-fume habituation, the little men appeared to be friendly gnomes and it was only after multiple experiences with gasoline inhalation that the gnomes became terrifying figures. Others have become horrified when visual hallucinations suggested that they were surrounded by fire or that molten metal was being poured over them.

These examples are not to suggest that terrifying hallucinations and illusions are necessarily a part of the experience. A few descriptions of pleasant experiences follow: "I lay in the grass looking up at the clouds. The clouds look like figures and statues and they go round and round." "Then I saw walls changing colors and they looked beautiful." "I started seeing colors. They glittered and I saw people's clothes changing colors." "The houses looked like pretty rocks in all colors and the windows were in colors and every house was in a different color and they were shining." These drugs are unpredictable—for some the images may be pleasant, vivid, and the experience characterized by hilarity and pleasure, whereas for others unpleasant feelings and hallucinations may predominate; but even those who have good experiences initially may suffer horrible hallucinations during a subsequent experience. At any rate, once the intoxication has occurred, continued sniffing or inhaling results in drowsiness and eventually unconsciousness.

During the last few years there have been speculations (especially in the press) that the problem is increasing massively. All the evidence is actually to the contrary. Young persons in this country have turned on with volatile materials since the latter part of the nineteenth century and the early part of this century, when groups used to get together for ether parties. In the early 1960s, glue-sniffing became a popular fad; for a while the problem increased and threatened to become serious, but figures from Chicago, Los Angeles and New York City are relatively reassuring. These figures and a considerable part of the data in this chapter are derived from an excellent article titled "Solvent Sniffing" by Drs. Edward Press and Alan K. Done, which appeared in *Pediatrics* in 1967. In Chicago there were 232 glue-sniffing arrests in 1963, rising to 476 in 1964, but the figure fell to 389 in 1965. In Los Angeles the figure for 1963 was 432, increasing to 623 in 1964 and dropping to 594 in 1965. In 1963 in New York City there were 2,003 glue-sniffing offenses. By 1964 this number had fallen to 1,307. On September 1, 1965 some relatively restrictive laws concerning volatile substances went into effect in New York State, making sale for purposes of intoxication a misdemeanor and possession for purposes of abuse a punishable offense. Unless the individual had a previous record of arrests he was referred to the youth division and no criminal charge was lodged. In 1965, the total of those referred to the youth division and those charged with an offense was 1,275, and for 1966 it was 1,547. The figures from these three cities, then, suggest that the problem is relatively stable.

Furthermore, in assessing the severity of the problem, it is extremely important to separate transient experimenters from habitual users. Those who experiment, do so out of curiosity, on a dare, or because their peers are inhaling. They are usually, but not always, boys from the lower socio-economic groups; their communal solvent-sniffing occurs one to several times, and ordinarily it does them no harm. This is not, of course, uniformly so. In New York City, for example, there have been several deaths attributed to glue-sniffing on roofs of buildings: the users lost their coordination, became dizzy and then fell several flights to the street below. Additionally, many individuals become reckless under the influence of these drugs, and some may engage either in aggressive or delinquent behavior.

Chronic sniffing of solvents is an entirely different problem. Here again, it characteristically occurs among lower socio-economic groups within which there is a high incidence of family disorganization. Often, there is virtually no father figure with whom the boy can identify, and characteristically the child has a poor record of school adjustment. Inhalation of volatile materials in these cases may start as early as three years of age, generally in reaction to anxieties generated by feelings of hostility or, in the older child, by sexual impulses. Many of these individuals are eventually diagnosed as either psychotic or as having schizoid personalities.

For the habitué, tolerance is often marked, meaning that it is necessary to take increasing amounts of the substance to achieve the same effects. Abrupt withdrawal can produce anxiety or depression, aggressive behavior, dizziness, nausea, insomnia and a fantastic craving to return to the drug. Loss of appetite is frequent, and as a result, some individuals may become strikingly cachectic, eventually taking on the appearance of prisoners in World War II concentration camps. Tremors, incoordination, memory loss, and irritation of the nose and eyes occur frequently, and in those who inhale gasoline, convulsions have been described. Antisocial acts are frequent, and range from truancy to shoplifting to occasional attempts at homicide.

In fact, the following cases of solvent-induced homicide are listed in the medical literature. A teen-age boy used thirteen tubes of glue, kidnapped a newly wed couple, killed the husband and raped the wife.

An eighteen-year-old boy, apparently in some sort of glue-sniffing induced panic, fatally stabbed a friend; he said that his friend had told him ghosts were coming into the room.

A homosexual boy under the influence of lacquer thinner killed a younger comrade. A sixteen-year-old boy under the influence of toluene-containing plastic cement shot a police officer. In Detroit, a fourteen-year-old boy participated in a glue-sniffing party and then raped and strangled two young sisters aged eight and six. Several months later an article headlined "Glue Sniffer Beats Murder Rap," noted that the boy was found innocent on the grounds that sniffing glue had made him temporarily insane. Granting that if a person is psychotic he can't be held legally responsible for his actions, it still seems that to virtually condone a heinous crime in a non-psychotic individual just because he happened to take a drug constitutes an abrogation of society's moral and legal responsibilities.

In addition to homicides, at least twenty other deaths have been reported in North America due to the effects of glue-sniffing. In nine of these the individual apparently suffocated in the bag held over his head to permit effective inhalation of the intoxicating substance. Others have died of acute brain and lung congestion. Recently lacquer-thinner-sniffing was blamed for five teen-age deaths in Japan, presumably due to the use of a similar mechanism. Many other adverse effects have been reported. Cases have been reported of individuals who inhaled gasoline fumes repeatedly and developed a psychosis very similar to that found in LSD users. A fifteen-year-old boy became violent under the influence of gasoline vapors and attacked a dog. Another, a nineteen-year-old boy, mewed like a cat, crying over and over again "I am having kittens." He slept in a pen with a pregnant sow, tried to choke his brother and threatened to kill his sister. There are frequently marked erotic overtones to the hallucinations and there may be striking sexual fantasies. In one case a sixteen-year-old boy had extraordinary sexual fantasies both homosexual and heterosexual in nature after inhaling gasoline vapors, and then frequently engaged in mutual masturbation with a friend.

The following few examples will further illustrate how very serious the results of inhaling volatile substances may be for certain individuals: In Ohio there were two deaths caused by inhalation of gasoline fumes when the gasoline exploded. A nineteen-year-old boy, a heavy gasoline sniffer, being unable to obtain any gasoline, used carbon tetrachloride which produced profound liver and kidney damage. Six young people chronically sniffed glue, the volatile substance of which was toluene, but in addition, the glue contained benzene—benzene being a noted depressant of the bone marrow. In these individuals the bone marrow did indeed become damaged, resulting in anemia from which all but one recovered. In the one, bone marrow depression was irreversible, and the patient, a fourteen-year-old boy, died of complicating anemia, bleeding and infection. Finally, there is a case of a young man who started inhaling toluene at age nineteen and became so habituated that he kept a small bottle of it in his pocket and continuously inhaled from a soaked rag throughout the day. After long use he developed irreversible brain damage, resulting in emotional instability, incoordination and defects in normal motor activity.

In summary, for most individuals, solvent-sniffing is indulged in only transiently and, except for occasional instances of injury, suffocation or violence, no permanent scar is left. A small number of individuals will become severely habituated, and for them glue- or gasoline-sniffing is a very serious problem which often results in aggression, violence or delinquent behavior, increases psychological isolation, accentuates personality defects, and may result in permanent brain dysfunction. Thus, solvent-sniffing is not to be taken lightly; but the data concerning the numbers involved suggest that it is not becoming a major problem. Indeed the apparent decrease of abuse in some areas may be attributed, at least in part, to laws which prohibit either the use of such materials for intoxication and/or mandate restrictions in sales.

Ups are of course amphetamine or other stimulants and downs are barbiturates or other sedatives, hypnotics or tranquilizers. Approximately 8 billion amphetamine pills or capsules are produced in the United States every year. This is enough to provide each person with 40 average doses. Analysis over a three-month period from June to August, 1967 revealed that between 2.6 and 3.9 per cent of all prescriptions written by physicians in the United States were for stimulants. Until February, 1966, when new federal drug control laws were implemented, literally millions of amphetamine pills or tablets could readily be obtained from a variety of firms in the United States, merely by sending and asking for them. It was estimated that approximately 50 per cent of all stimulants produced in the United States were diverted to the illicit market selling for 10 cents to $1 per pill. The increasing use of stimulants is a world-wide problem which arose after World War II. In Japan in 1954 there were between 500,000 and 600,000 users of amphetamines, 300,000 of whom took the drug intravenously. Great Britain has recognized the problem since approximately 1958, and in Sweden there is currently an extraordinary epidemic, described in detail in Chapter 5.

In the United States, amphetamine abuse appears to be increasing among several groups. Many people—college students, housewives, etc.—obtain their drugs legitimately and subsequently use them indiscriminately. Students use them, for the most part, at exam time. In one girl's college in New York State it is estimated that 40 per cent of the students take amphetamines illicitly. However, this is not a major or worrisome form of abuse, does not result in dependency and does not lead to other drugs. It may, of course, create problems for the individual. There are a substantial number of cases on record in which a student took repeated doses of oral amphetamines prior to an exam in order to study intensively and wrote what he or she thought to be a magnificent paper, only to discover later either that the entire two- or three-hour exam had been written on one line or that a single sentence had been written over and over again. These complications are fortunately infrequent.

Housewives use the drug for weight reduction or merely to relieve feelings of fatigue. The overwhelming majority get into no trouble doing this, but it certainly sets bad examples for their children. Truck drivers are known to gobble large amounts of amphetamines prior to taking long trips, and an increasing number of automobile accidents have been ascribed to this practice.

On an entirely different level is the use of amphetamines by heroin addicts. For decades many heroin users preferentially have used a combination of heroin and cocaine called speedballs. When the combination is taken intravenously, the action of the cocaine is very rapid, the user experiences a so-called rush in the lower abdomen or genitalia, and this is followed by the prolonged lassitude induced by heroin. Since cocaine is difficult to obtain and is expensive, many heroin addicts began changing to the use of amphetamines, taking the stimulant not in pill form but intravenously as methamphetamine. This is sold legally or illegally as a liquid or can be bought illicitly in crystalline form and is popularly known as "crystals." The commercial name of the most popular preparation is Methedrine. Alternately an identical material caled Desoxyn is used. Interestingly, although Methedrine and Desoxyn contain precisely the same drugs in the same concentrations, users will tell you that they are strikingly different and generally express a preference for Methedrine, again emphasizing the important psychological and ritualistic aspects of drug abuse. In the United States and England many of the opiate addicts using heroin and amphetamines together have become amphetamine habitués and now use it as the drug of choice. This is not surprising; intravenously administered amphetamines are highly stimulating, act as energizers and often, though not predictably, increase sexual drive and/or performance. When heroin and amphetamines are taken together intravenously, the major effect is not of the heroin but rather of the amphetamines, which, taken in large doses, have about the same duration of action as heroin, so that the opiate is almost entirely masked. Many of the heroin users get conditioned to the stimulating amphetamine kick, and afterwards tend to use that preferentially. When amphetamines are taken orally for legitimate purposes, 5 milligrams three times a day is a substantial dose. Taken intravenously as methamphetamine, 20 to 40 milligrams are used three to four times a day, but as the individual becomes accustomed to the drug this is often increased to 100 to 300 milligrams per injection or 20 to 60 times the average oral dose. Some individuals, through constant use, develop a tolerance for the drug and must use increasing amounts to achieve the same effects. Under these conditions habitués have taken as much as 1,000 milligrams in one injection. According to an article by Drs. John Kramer, Vitezslav Fischman and Don Littlefield in the *Journal of the American Medical Association* in July, 1967, the largest amount used in any twenty-four-hour period by a habitué was estimated to be close to 15,000 milligrams, or one thousand times the normal amount taken by mouth. Although intravenous amphetamine use is fairly extensive among New York City addicts, the practice is more prevalent among heroin addicts in California, where the practice started after physicians prescribed injectable methamphetamine to addicts, apparently with the misguided notion that this would benefit the opiate addiction. Subsequently, the addicts found that they could obtain crystalline methamphetamine directly by representing themselves as individuals engaged in pharmacological research. This source has now been at least partially eliminated, and the addicts rely on illicitly manufactured amphetamines, enough being produced to keep California well inundated with the drug. Since the effects are described in detail in Chapter 5, I shall merely summarize the ones reported by Dr. Kramer and his colleagues. They noted that the initial sensation of extreme physical and mental power was replaced by emotional lability as well as confusing and frightening perceptions. Illusions and hallucinations appeared; almost uniformly the users developed feelings of persecution. One of their patients took out his Doberman dog every night in order to track down his imaginary enemies. Another barricaded himself in an apartment and installed a complicated system of booby traps and electrical alarm devices in order to outwit the police, who in fact were neither aware of, nor interested in, his activities. Other forms of compulsive behavior are common. For example, those who are mechanically minded may spend many hours dismantling and reassembling gadgets which are in perfect order. Heavy intravenous users often continued without sleep for one or two weeks; this period is followed by prolonged sleep before returning to another run of amphetamine use.

Use of amphetamines is also increasing strikingly among hippies. Hippies use both oral amphetamines and intravenous Methedrine or Desoxyn. They tend to use marihuana and LSD first, and subsequently turn to stimulants. Among these persons, the use of amphetamines either by mouth or injection tends to be less constant than among the intravenous heroin users. They are more likely to intermix pills and injections in indiscriminate fashion, but are less likely to have extended runs of intravenous amphetamine use.

The following is a reasonably typical case recently observed in New York City. A twenty-three-year-old was hospitalized because of hepatitis. At the age of nineteen she had attended college in Los Angeles and become attached to a hippie group. She first started using marihuana and then, without having taken oral amphetamines, began to use intravenous Methedrine, taking the drug intermittently. She was careful to point out that unlike some of her friends, she never developed a heavy Methedrine habit. She also noted that virtually her entire coterie of hippie friends used intravenous amphetamines to a greater or lesser degree. Under its influence she would walk long distances or paint for hours at a time, claiming that her ability to concentrate was much enhanced by the drug. When I asked her whether she found the drug sexually stimulating she appeared surprised and said that although she personally engaged in considerable sexual activity, the drug had no effect on her; nor was she aware of any effect on her Methedrine-using friends. Subsequent to Methedrine use she began to take large amounts of LSD, having both good and bad trips but without severe consequences. Following some marital difficulties, she returned to New York City, where she found that both Methedrine and Desoxyn were readily available. However, after joining a Greenwich Village crowd she switched her allegiance to a delinquent group on the West Side of Manhattan who were not amphetamine users but did take heroin. One of the boys in the group gave her her wings (injected her with intravenous heroin) on three or four occasions; she subsequently became addicted, eventually increasing her dosage to as much as fifty bags of heroin daily, which by American standards is an extraordinarily large dose. Finally, tiring of this life, she voluntarily signed herself into a rehabilitation program, was found to be jaundiced and was hospitalized for what subsequently turned out to be relatively severe liver damage. Amphetamine use is also characteristic of certain delinquent groups, especially motorcycle gangs such as the Hell's Angels.

Hunter Thompson in his book, *Hell's Angels*, points out that bennies (amphetamines) are basic to the outlaw diet, and that the same individuals use barbiturates, including seconal, amytal and nembutal which are known as reds, blue heavens and yellow jackets respectively. These delinquent groups use amphetamine pills far more than they use intravenous methamphetamine. Large amounts are consumed and under their influence delinquent and aggressive behavior is frequently carried out. Other activities include the destroying of property, gang attacks on people they feel convinced cannot fight back effectively, rapes and gang orgies.

The use of amphetamines to achieve an "up" is paralleled by the use of barbiturates to achieve a "down." In 1962 enough barbiturates were produced in the United States to supply twenty-four average doses to every man, woman and child in the country. Although there is obviously a great deal of over-prescribing by physicians and considerable illicit use, there is no indication that at present this is a major or rapidly growing problem. There is some abuse among high school students and considerable use by delinquent groups, such as motorcycle gangs. Additionally, hippies who will take almost anything to become intoxicated, consume substantial amounts of barbiturates or tranquilizers as do narcotic addicts who use supplemental oral and intravenous barbiturates to prolong the heroin effect. In a study in 1964, 23 per cent of narcotic addicts admitted to one hospital were found to be simultaneously dependent on barbiturates. This is a very serious problem because, if not recognized, acute withdrawal from barbiturates can produce an overwhelming, even lethal, abstinence syndrome. At the outset, the drugs produce relaxation and reduction in anxiety. However, once the individual gets habituated to either oral or intravenously administered barbiturates, he experiences striking mood shifts without apparent cause, irritability, self-neglect, infantile behavior, incoordination, difficulty in speaking and profound impairment of judgment, ability to concentrate and intellectual capacity. If the drug is then abruptly stopped, the individual becomes restless, anxious, irritable, and unable to sleep; the heart rate increases strikingly and body temperature may rise to as high as 105 degrees. When this happens, the blood pressure may drop, the patient may become comatose and may experience repeated generalized convulsions. If he is not given barbiturates promptly, death may ensue. Among those who are simultaneously addicted to barbiturates and heroin, the withdrawal from heroin is now relatively easy whereas withdrawing the individual from barbiturates may be prolonged, difficult and, if done ineptly, fraught with dangers.

Except then for mild to moderate abuse in schools and heavy use among hippies, some delinquents, and heroin-addicted persons, as well as some individuals with underlying severe psychiatric disorders, the increase in barbiturate use is primarily a manifestation of our national drug-oriented hypochondriasis and is symptomatic of the current American belief that virtually every problem can be solved or amelioriated by some pill or injection.

A number of other substances have seen some use in the unending search for ups and downs. Aspirin or fingernail polish remover is mixed with Coca-Cola; anti-motion-sickness pills are taken with beer; nasal decongestant tablets containing a mild stimulant are ingested in large numbers; or the stimulant-containing cotton plugs or impregnated papers are removed from

nasal inhalers and swallowed with water, Coca-Cola or
beer. Lately, banana peel scrapings, nutmegs and Freon
have all been in the news. Whether the banana peel
scrapings actually contain a hallucinogenic agent is not
known, but in any case the kick is small and this fad
seems to be disappearing as suddenly as it started.
Nutmeg intoxication is a slightly different story. Nutmegs are obtained from the evergreen tree, *myristica
fragrans,* and have been used in Arabian and Indian
medicine since the second or third century. At that time
the potion was given for a farrago of illnesses and, as
one might expect, it was prescribed as an aphrodisiac,
although its potential in this regard appears to be virtually nil. The first pharmacological experiments with
nutmeg were performed in the seventeenth century by
the noted scientist van Leeuwenhoek and since that
time it has been known that nutmeg intoxication causes
nausea, palpitations, dry mouth, incoherence, a reddish
appearance to the face, hyperactivity, increased blood
pressure and on occasion even stupor and delirium. A
dosage of one to two teaspoons, a modest amount,
usually produces a reaction similar to marihuana, but
nutmeg's undesirable side effects and toxicity have limited its popularity. A small number of cases of intoxication requiring medical aid have been described among
college students, but it seems unlikely that nutmeg use
will increase significantly among the intoxicant-prone in
the United States.

Freon and similar materials are used in chilling glas-
ses. When Freon is used appropriately it is nontoxic.
However, young people found that when inhaled it
produces a kick which they attribute to the drug, but
which in actuality is due to the drug's displacement of
oxygen in the lungs. The effects then result from lowered oxygen supply to the brain. When deliberately
directly inhaled, it may literally freeze the respiratory
tract and cause death by asphyxiation. This happened
in mid-1967 in seven cases, including one involving a

twenty-one-year-old Bucknell University student and an eleven-year-old girl given the material by her older brother. In this instance use was abetted by the usual irresponsible publicity, this time in an Eastern college newspaper which told all about the new "safe" kick. That's some kick to advertise—its effects due to anoxia and its major side reaction death by asphyxiation.

Between 1967 and 1969, a total of over twenty persons died from inhalants. Finally, in mid-1969, the drug subculture admitted that Freon might cause asphyxiation but suggested that this complication could be obviated by either letting Freon come to room temperature or heating it gently. In urging Freon upon young people, once again they are ignoring two points. First, half the deaths were due to lowered oxygen to the brain, not asphyxiation. Second, if you heat Freon, even gently, it is likely to explode.

CHAPTER FOUR

THE LONDON SCENE

In 1926 the Departmental Committee on Morphine and Heroin Addiction, popularly known as the Rolleston Committee, established opiate regulations for both physicians and users. In essence, this report legitimatized administration by physicians of heroin and cocaine to addicts—but only after assiduous efforts had been made to withdraw the individual from his drugs. Central to the Rolleston Committee's recommendations was the concept that withdrawal was the preferred treatment but that a patient could be maintained on drugs if withdrawal produced such severe symptomatology that it could not be accomplished satisfactorily or if, upon withdrawal, the addict was unable to lead a fairly normal and useful life. The committee felt that although withdrawal was clearly the desired goal, maintenance therapy could be countenanced if it permitted the individual to remain as a functioning, productive member of society. In the United States the Rolleston Report has been hailed as the epitome of common sense and humanitarianism, and it has been widely assumed that these regulations have resulted in a lessening of the narcotics problem in England. In fact, England had no problem at the time of the report. It is, therefore, illogical to claim, as some do, that the English cured their problem by following the committee's recommendations.

In 1962, Edwin Schur wrote a book entitled, *Narcot-*

ic Addiction in Britain and America: The Impact of Public Policy, in which, based on a two-year study in the late 1950s he extolled the British system and condemned the more restrictive punitively-oriented American approach. As noted above, one of the objectives of the Rolleston Committee was social rehabilitation with or without drugs, and even Schur in his now heavily criticized book admits that his investigations showed that people being maintained on opiates had very poor work records and, therefore, were not optimally rehabilitated.

Even as Schur was pointing out that England had no problem, the situation was changing. In 1936, there were in Great Britain 566 known opiate addicts. This figure fell to 500 in 1939, and immediately after World War II, in 1947, further diminished to 191. By 1950, the number had risen again to 217, and there was an additional increase to 332 by 1958. By 1960 the figure had reached 424. Still, the problem was small compared to that in the United States; moreover, at the time of the Schur book, the virtually simultaneous 1961 report of the Inter-departmental Committee on Drug Addiction, popularly known as the Brain Committee, ascribed the modest increase between 1950 and 1960 to greater recognition and detection and this was not considered to be a matter of concern.

This blissful situation was not to continue for long. A second report from the Inter-Committee in 1965, noted a remarkable increase in the number of heroin and cocaine users. Meanwhile, Dr. Philip Connell, of the Maudsley Hospital in London, had observed substantial abuse of amphetamines, and by the summer of 1966 the British authorities recognized that the drug problem in their country was becoming serious. Under the aegis of the British Society for the Study of Addiction a major conference was planned for London in early September, 1966. Several Americans, myself among them, were invited to summarize various aspects of drug abuse in the United States and to outline our approach to these problems. Of course, to us it all seemed a bit ludicrous. For years a potpourri of sociologists, psychologists, politicians and physicians had been condemning, with varying degrees of asperity, the American approach to these problems and using the British approach as an example of a humane, intelligent and successful program. Now, suddenly, the American experts were being summoned to help the English attack their burgeoning drug abuse problem. And summon is indeed the appropriate word. I had just returned from a speaking engagement in Holland, and was scheduled to speak in both Czechoslovakia and Scotland in the month of October. Consequently, I had no intention of rushing to England for a two-day conference. However, the British were not about to accept a no. I received a call from the conveners of the conference emphasizing the concern in England and noting that in good conscience we in America who had substantial experience with the problems could not refuse the invitation.

Refusal being clearly inadvisable, I attended what turned out to be a fascinating conference, and then, in October, 1967 and November, 1969 I returned to London for brief but intensive surveys of their current drug problem.

In England the major increases have been in the use of cannabis and heroin. The heroin statistics as provided by the British Home Office are truly extraordinary. Between 1944 and 1954, a ten-year period, a total of only 44 *new* cases of heroin addiction were reported, an average of less than five new cases each year. In the next five years the rate almost doubled— 49 being reported in that five-year span. Starting in

1960, the number of new cases began to grow dramatically, increasing substantially in every year thereafter.

The figures for the period 1961-1966 are as follows:

YEAR	NEW CASES REPORTED
1961	56
1962	72
1963	90
1964	162
1965	259
1966	522

In other words, in 1966 there were more new heroin addicts reported than in the entire twenty-year span between 1945 and 1964. Currently there are approximately 3,000 heroin addicts known to the Home Office and the accepted estimate indicates that in actuality there are perhaps double that number, or approximately 6,000. This figure is, of course, well below the approximately 100,000 addicts estimated in the United States. Taking into account the population differences between Great Britain and the United States, our problem is six to seven times as great. However, the crucial fact to keep in mind is that their problem is growing precipitously and ours has not changed dramatically in the past fifteen years.

In part, the profound increase in England is clearly due to over-prescribing by physicians. Only a small number of physicians were involved, the 1965 report referring to six who were particularly at fault. The amount of heroin given out by these doctors was enormous; for example, in 1962 one physician prescribed some 600,000 tablets of heroin, or 6 million milligrams. In the United States this would permit approximately 200,000 individual intravenous doses. This same doctor on one occasion prescribed 900 tablets (9,000 milligrams) to a single addict. With the understanding that in the United States an addict might use 75 milligrams per day, the enormity

The London Scene 61

of the prescription becomes apparent. Worse still, three days later the same doctor prescribed for the same patient an additional 6,000 milligrams to "replace pills lost in an accident." Another physician was for a long time literally operating out of the London subway system, and behaved much as if he were selling candy. Virtually anyone could go up to him, say he wanted heroin or cocaine, pay him approximately $8 as a "consultant fee" and receive a prescription for as much heroin or cocaine as he wanted. In October, 1967 the same physician was continuing his indiscriminate operation but was now working out of a hotel room instead of the London underground.

The dynamics of the British epidemic appear clear. Initially a neophyte will obtain his drug from other addicts who are receiving it legally from physicians. Many of these were given, for example, two or three hundred milligrams per day, half of which they used and the other half of which they sold or gave away. After a period of months, the neophyte becomes addicted. He then registers with a physician and begins to receive his heroin and cocaine by prescription. According to one study, the average heroin dose for such addicts is 4.3 grains per day, or approximately 260 milligrams. The British addicts are thus at least as heavily addicted as their American counterparts, whose average dose is in the range of 75 milligrams daily.

There are several points of interest about the British heroin addict. Prior to settling on heroin he has an even more catholic taste in drugs than his American counterpart. In a recent series consisting of 92 patients, 79 had used marihuana prior to becoming addicted to heroin, 59 had used oral amphetamines, 21 had been excessive users of alcohol and smaller numbers had used LSD, cocaine and intravenous amphetamines. This appears to be very typical of the British drug scene. Those who use cannabis, amphetamines or LSD may on occasion try heroin, although without ever becoming addicted. Similarly, those who become addicted to heroin may try LSD either before or after their addiction, a phenomenon found less frequently in the United States where there has been relatively little overlap between heroin addicts and LSD users. Once addicted to heroin, the individual characteristically uses a stimulant, cocaine being the most common.

The British heroin addict, although generally from lower economic groups, is likely to have completed a major part or all of his high school education and to have some job skills even if he doesn't work. In both these respects he differs from most American addicts. However, heroin use is not by any means confined to lower economic groups. It is found in all social strata, with middle- and upper-class groups being represented, proportionately, to a far greater degree than in America, where only small numbers of middle- and upper-class individuals use heroin. In fact, in many of the major universities in England there are small numbers of heroin addicts. Indeed, one of the collegiate drug scandals involved the death of a close relative of a former Prime Minister, apparently as the result of suffocation secondary to heroin overdose. This again contrasts with the United States, where heroin addiction among individuals remaining in college has been extraordinarily infrequent. In 1969, of course, the American scene began to change; heroin use expanded to involve substantial numbers of affluent persons and invaded American high schools and colleges.

I was told also of a particularly pernicious form of heroin abuse among a small number of women addicts, who deliberately introduced their sexual partners to heroin in order to make the man dependent upon them. Once this has occurred, however, and the men are addicted, the women lose interest in retaining them, break off the relationship and start over with somebody else.

Several studies show that the medical complication

rate among the heroin-cocaine users is enormous. In one series of 100 consecutive cases collected by Drs. T. H. Bewley and O. Ben-Arie of the Tooting Bec Hospital, 29 had hepatitis, 22 abscesses, 21 psychoses due to cocaine, amphetamines or LSD, 17 overdose reactions and 4 septicemia (blood stream infection). There were 12 deaths in the series, 7 of these due either to opiate or barbiturate overdose. A careful analysis of 35 deaths in male heroin addicts by Dr. I. Pierce James was published in December, 1967, in the British *Journal of Addiction*. Of the 35, 9 died of suicide and 12 of narcotic overdose, the average age at death being approximately 28 years. In this group receiving their medicines on prescription, supposedly under controlled circumstances, the death rate was fantastically high— twenty times the expected, with a suicide rate fifty times the expected.

One of the major medical complications of heroin addiction in the United States is hepatitis, a virus infection of the liver, transmitted in this case by unsterile needles. At Bellevue Hospital, in New York City, for example, more than half of all cases of hepatitis occur in main-line (intravenously administered) heroin users. Futhermore, liver function tests and/or biopsies reveal the presence of hepatitis in over 75 per cent of chronic heroin abusers. One might have assumed that the incidence of hepatitis would be substantially less in England since the drug is given out by physicians, and sterile needles and syringes are readily obtainable. Apparently, this is not the case. In a study of some 280 British heroin users, 60 per cent showed either abnormal liver function tests or overt jaundice presumably due in each case to virus hepatitis resulting from the use of unsterile materials. This is not difficult to understand in the view of the addicts' insistence on egregiously unhygienic techniques and the sharing of needles.

The British addicts' approach to sterilization is illustrated by the following two stories. One young addict was participating in a study of liver function which required that a blood specimen be obtained from him. However, he had used drugs for so long that his veins were scarred to a degree that made it impossible for the physicians to successfully draw blood. The addict himself then observed that he knew his veins best and volunteered to obtain the specimen. His arm was prepared, he found the vein he wanted, picked up the syringe and, just before attempting to obtain blood, quickly brought the needle and syringe up to his mouth and licked the needle, noting that this somewhat less than acceptable technique always enhanced his ability to find his own veins.

Another addict, having used his prescription supply rapidly, was tremulous and nervous when he obtained a new supply from the pharmacy. Rushing outside, he found a public toilet and went into one of the stanchions to inject himself with his heroin and cocaine. He filled his syringe, but just as he was about to inject himself, his tremors got the better of him and he dropped the syringe and needle. He stood panic-stricken as he watched the syringe break and his precious heroin ooze out onto the floor, fully recognizing that he no longer had the tools with which to inject himself. As his horror grew, he was comforted by a voice in the next stanchion saying, "Don't worry; have a go at mine," and with that, a hand reached across the dividing partition to pass him a syringe and needle; the needle was still dripping with blood, having just been used by the addict in the next stall. Needless to say, there could be no better way of spreading hepatitis than by this needle-sharing camaraderie.

There has been no attempt at all in England to rehabilitate the addict and return him to society. For the hospitalized heroin user there is some group therapy, which in certain cases merely amounts to a reliving of the drug experience, thus increasing the longing for a return to the drug. No attempts at job rehabilitation or placement have been made, and as a result the addict obtaining his drugs legally on prescription sits around the pubs taking drugs and doing little else. He uses whatever amount of drugs he needs for his own habit, gives the rest away or sells it to obtain money for his food, clothing and lodging. Some receive welfare, but in England such assistance is prohibited unless one has a home address. Many addicts have either left home or have been thrown out of their living quarters and consequently lead a footloose life, without official home address, which disqualifies them from welfare payments. They therefore subsist primarily by selling the heroin and cocaine and naturally welcome a new market, which leads to further indoctrination of neophytes into the vicissitudes of heroin use.

It is hardly surprising the so-called English system has failed. After all, if you have a group of people receiving drugs who do not work and are not constructive members of society, who merely sit around the pubs taking drugs, talking drugs, selling drugs, giving drugs away and increasing the size of their sub-culture, the problem is bound to increase. But the massive increase in heroin use in England is only part of the story. For over the last five years, there has been a remarkable escalation in the use of all drugs.

The increase is well illustrated by the figures on cannabis. The form of cannabis used in England is hashish, which is perhaps five to eight times as potent as American marihuana. The hashish comes in small bricks of pure resin ranging in colors from brown to black. In the United States it is very easy to get marihuana and usually quite difficult to get hashish, whereas in England the situation is reversed. Between 1945 and 1961 cannabis offenses grew steadily but unspectacularly; by 1961 there were 288 offenses and of these, 220 occured among immigrants and only 68 among native-born British persons. In the next five years the picture changed dramatically. Each year the total number of offenses rose, so that by 1966 there were 1,119 total cannabis offenses, 352 of which were among immigrants and 767 among native-born white Englishmen. Here again abuse was spread throughout the population. Some health officials close to the situation estimate that at the University of London approximately 15 per cent of the students have had experience with hashish. A recent study of 232 patients admitted to a venereal disease clinic in London showed that 18.2 per cent used drugs, the most popular being hashish.

Hashish is not always an innocuous drug. Severe hallucinations, acute intoxication and personality deterioration have all been described, as have acute or subacute psychoses, though the feeling in regard to the latter is that the individuals had long-standing personality defects which deteriorated further under the influence of hashish. Although heroin users can generally be described as comprising a delinquent group with disturbed personalities, the hashish users cannot be readily classified. Lonely or rebellious persons, students, professors, businessmen, fringe groups, beatniks and the flower people all use hashish, which is relatively inexpensive in London, two cigarettes costing $1.40.

The use of LSD is clearly increasing, although no precise figures are available as to the number of people involved. Many of the users are found among the hippie, beatnik and flower groups, but not uniformly so. There is some student experimentation and, additionally, a surprisingly large percentage of those addicted to heroin have had experience with LSD, particularly among those who for one reason or another have tired of their heroin habit.

There is general agreement that one of the major mechanisms of increase in LSD abuse has been injudicious and uncritical publicity both in the press and on television. The LSD problem surfaced in England almost two years after it became serious in the United States and, as in America, the initial publicity has tended to concentrate on the pleasurable effects, the hallucinations, transcendental experiences and other positive facets, minimizing the enormous dangers. Additionally, experimentation with both hashish and LSD appears to have grown because of an enormous amount of publicity given to the use of these drugs by popular music groups such as the Beatles and the Rolling Stones. The result has been increasing use, especially among unstable, insecure or sociopathic personalities.

In England a great many people sell small amounts of hashish and LSD. These individuals (who have no record of other criminal activity) become traffickers simply for profit, as part of a socializing behavior pattern, or as proselytizers. Although these individuals do not appear to be part of a major criminal conspiracy such as occurs with heroin in the United States, the organized criminal elements do participate in the drug rackets, primarily by operating dance halls, coffee shops, etc., which serve as centers for distribution of the drugs. In England, as in America, the determination to turn other people on is an important aspect of drug spread. In a series of 232 patients studied in a venereal disease clinic, one-fifth of those who used drugs said that they would personally give them to younger teenage brothers or sisters.

The final major drug problem in England relates to use of amphetamines, taken orally or intravenously. Although this too is increasing, precise figures are not known. It is, however, thought that some 20,000 persons in England are dependent on either oral or intravenous amphetamines. Again, the increasing use appears to occur at multiple levels in British society. Bohemians, hippies and flower people are both using pills and injecting Methedrine.

Lower economic, often delinquent, groups have been using amphetamines, primarily at weekend parties, for at least 14 years; this usage seems to be growing, along with pill-taking in the high schools. Furthermore, many cocaine-using heroin addicts have been withdrawn from cocaine by substituting intravenous methamphetamine (Methedrine), and others who used only opiates (no stimulants) have been given stimulants as therapy for their opiate addiction. Liking the amphetamine kick, some now use large amounts of the drug intravenously.

Changing the addict from cocaine to intravenous amphetamines or trying to treat heroin addiction with stimulants is in no way beneficial. As will be discussed subsequently, intravenously administered central stimulants such as Methedrine are enormously toxic. In large part, the administration of amphetamines under these conditions appears to be related to ignorance on the part of physicians about the very high complication rate. I was told by one of the physicians involved that so much Methedrine was being prescribed in 1966-1967 that the pharmaceutical firms have been compelled to increase their output, much of which is either diverted to the illicit market directly, or indirectly by the users themselves after receiving the drug on prescription from unwary physicians. The availability of the drug abetted the spread of intravenous use beyond the heroin addict population to delinquent and hippie groups, as well as those who use it deliberately for potential sexual stimulation.

Characteristically, intravenous users take three to five ampules a day by injection, each ampule containing 30 milligrams. As with Methedrine, amphetamine pills are readily available, selling for 14 to 20 cents each. Some people have become severe amphetamine habitués merely because they were searching for hashish, could not find it and decided to try any other drug which would get them high.

There appear to be some valid reasons for separating intravenous Methedrine users from those who use excessive amounts of amphetamines by mouth, the former tending to be more delinquent and to have greater personality disturbances.

The increase in abuse of all drugs in England suggests that merely tightening the regulations for prescription of heroin will not in any way solve the problem. Indeed, in regard to heroin, if legalized prescribing is markedly restricted, it appears likely that an illegal black market will develop. The most impressive aspect of the British scene is the tendency for the drug user to try a great many drugs; consequently, the use of any specific agent is found in all segments of society. There seemed little doubt in 1967 that the abuse of amphetamines, cannabis and LSD would increase markedly over the next few years, in part because there is an increasing tendency in British society for young people to feel that they can solve or avert their problems through drug intoxication.

London in recent years has been known as a swinging city and, along with its sea of miniskirts, has developed a substantial hippie population. I spent one night in 1967 viewing their best psychedelic show in an austere old brick building called the Round House. Everybody was doing his or her thing which ranged from watching artistic motion pictures, off-beat humorous movies, delightful moving psychedelic abstractions, or pulsating moving lightbeams, to wild rock-and-roll dancing, uninhibited stripteases, etc. The rules of the club prohibited drug-taking within the Round House, and there was such fear of a police raid that, as far as I could tell, this rule was quite rigidly adhered to. Nevertheless, many people there were clearly stoned, and I was told that the usual technique was to take hashish, amphetamines or LSD before coming to the club. It does seem quite clear that among the English hippies, drug-taking is an integral part of their lives. This movement is spreading in England and with it, ineluctably, drug abuse will spread. England has always felt that it had less of a drug problem than we do here in the United States, but as of October, 1967, they appeared to have as much abuse of cannabis and amphetamines as we do, and they were rapidly catching up to us in the use of heroin and LSD.

By the fall of 1969, the British scene had changed in several ways. First, in April, 1968, they abandoned their much abused prescribing system. Now addicts must receive their drugs from special clinics in which a vigorous attempt is made to reduce the total dosage. A black market in heroin and cocaine has sprung up and the number of addicts continues to grow, but many in England believe they are beginning to cope with the problem better now that the free prescribing system has been abandoned. Second, cannabis and LSD use is increasing although the latter, as in America, appears to be reaching a plateau. Third, the British reacted in characteristically sensible fashion to the excessive use of Methedrine. The medical profession, government and pharmaceutical companies got together and decided that since Methedrine was being obtained from physicians or by diversion of the legal supply, the best solution was to reduce the supply. And so they did. Now physicians cannot administer Methedrine in their offices and cannot write prescriptions for it. It can be dispensed only from clinics or hospitals. Physicians have accepted this restriction on their prescribing and the drug subculture has accepted for the most part the medical judgment that intravenous speed is too dangerous to play around with. As a result, supply is down, a major black market has developed and England appears well on the way to coping reasonably well with the Methedrine problem—at least as of fall of 1969.

CHAPTER FIVE

TURNING ON IN STOCKHOLM

On the morning of September 25, 1967, as I left London aboard a British European Airways plane bound for Stockholm, I believed it would be possible to review the Swedish drug situation in two days, leaving me three days to explore the charms of Stockholm, a bustling and delightful city. I could not have been more wrong. For, unknowingly, I was stepping directly into the center of perhaps the most vitriolic drug controversy in the world at the present time. I was greeted at the airport by an ebullient and embattled Swedish psychiatrist, one of the protagonists in a monumental struggle which threatens to rock all of Sweden. We had met only briefly a year before in London and I had had the usual qualms about whether our conversation would now be easy-flowing or strained. I need not have worried. During the entire forty-five-minute trip back to my hotel in Stockholm I sat virtually silent and literally open-mouthed as his version of Sweden's central-stimulant problem erupted from him with volcanic intensity. When we got to my hotel he waited in the car while I hurriedly checked in; he then took me to his house, where in the course of several hours he detailed the incredible and intriguing story of the Swedish epidemic.

Anxious for my support, he set up meetings for me over the next four days with virtually every important individual involved in the fight, on both sides, as well as interviews with patients and their relatives. What impressed me most during these many interviews was the utter frankness of all of the people I talked with and their willingness to provide me with the minutest details of their actions and records over the last three years. As a result, I think I was able to get a very accurate picture of the Swedish problem. In detailing it I shall deliberately not use individual names, at least for the most part, because in some cases it might be embarrassing and would in no way enhance the story.

Let me make it clear that Sweden's major problem is that of intravenously administered central stimulants of the amphetamine type. They do have, however, an increasing problem with cannabis, mainly in the form of hashish; one study of Stockholm high school students showed that almost 20 per cent had used it on at least one occasion. This figure is generally considered to be high; the average use in Stockholm high schools is thought to be somewhere between 5 and 15 per cent, and for the country as a whole somewhat over 2 per cent. Students, hippies, artists and fringe groups all use hashish, and although some intoxication has been noted, this is not considered a serious problem. There is a mild increase in the use of LSD and other potent hallucinogens, but at present only relatively small numbers are involved. It seems likely, though, that this problem will increase, as most of the publicity accorded LSD so far has been favorable. In regard to opiates, there are now in all of Sweden approximately one hundred addicts, who for the most part use morphine. This represents perhaps a threefold increase over the last few years, but opiate addiction is also not felt to be a major problem. Indeed, the most interesting aspect of opiate abuse is that the majority of the users concurrently use large amounts of central stimulants.

The chronology of the central-stimulant problem itself is approximately as follows: In the late 1940's the use of amphetamines by mouth became popular among

a very small group of artists and bohemians. During the
next five years this group grew slowly, and as it grew,
the amount of amphetamines taken by mouth also increased for the individuals involved. Then, according to
one story, an overaged medical student got the bright
idea of using stimulants intravenously. The kick was
found to be substantially greater under these conditions, and by 1954 there were an estimated 200 individuals who took intravenous central stimulants. There
was a rash of publicity about the usage in 1954, but by
1958 the experts were saying that there was no problem
at all. Despite these pronouncements, the number of
users increased to an estimated 1,000 by 1960, and
approximately 2,000 by 1964.

The stimulant used in recent years has almost exclusively been phenmetrazine, the trade name of which is
Preludin. Although an artistic bohemian group started
the use of the drug, by 1964 it was localized almost
entirely among a delinquent population similar to the
heroin population in the United States. Preludin is a
psychic energizer, which gained popularity as a medication to help in weight reduction. The average oral dose
is one 25-milligram pill three times a day, whereas
intravenous users dissolve 10 to 40 pills in water, filter
the suspension through gauze and then inject it directly
into a vein. Once they are fully habituated they tend to
give themselves from 3 to 6 injections a day, utilizing a
total of 75 to 400 pills. Preludin taken intravenously in
this fashion gives a tremendous kick. All sensations are
massively heightened, colors become incredibly vivid,
and sounds become so augmented that the individual
may insist that other people in the room whisper,
claiming that the spoken voice is unpleasantly intense.
Food taste is so accentuated that spicy foods may seem
piquant to the point of unpleasantness. Standing next to
a woman, the user may find her perfume virtually
overwhelming, and by the same token may be so aware
of the body odors of others that he cannot remain in

close proximity or sometimes even in the same room with them. Along with the profound accentuation of all sensations, the users become incredibly overactive, energetic and totally incapable of sleeping. During a central-stimulant binge they may remain awake literally for days or weeks at a time, injecting themselves every few hours with increasing doses of Preludin until they develop a tolerance and no longer get an effect. Then, they inject themselves intravenously with a barbiturate, discontinue the central stimulants, fall into a deep and sometimes agitated sleep, finally waking with an abstinence syndrome that results in an intense craving for more Preludin. The abstinence syndrome is characterized by anxiety, a dry mouth, extreme restlessness, nervousness and sometimes marked twitching of the fingers, extremities or even the head. If they can get more Preludin, they then start on another jag which may again last for many days or weeks.

All of the central stimulants, notably Methedrine, Preludin and methylphenidate (a stimulant commercially called Ritalin) are said to have a substantial aphrodisiac effect. The effect appears to be least predictable with Methedrine, the central stimulant widely used in the United States and Britain, and far more marked with Ritalin and Preludin. For aphrodisiac purposes, most but not all of the Swedish habitués prefer Preludin to Ritalin.

I learned more about this aspect of Preludin use from Sweden's world-renowned forensic psychiatrist, Professor Gösta Rylander, a tall, gray-haired, distinguished-looking and articulate man. Professor Rylander had studied intensively a large number of patients taking central stimulants and was most knowledgeable about the sexual effects of Preludin, which he felt to be one of the most potent aphrodisiacs known to man. We had an animated conversation over lunch at a Stockholm restaurant, and then

Professor Rylander began to detail in an enthusiastic and loud tone of voice the sexual effects of Preludin. As a somewhat conventional and inhibited American, well aware that Swedes almost always understand English, I began to wonder what the other people in the restaurant must think of our vigorous sexually oriented conversation, but my modest embarrassment became acute as the eminent Professor Rylander turned on me and said in about as loud a voice as he could, "As a matter of fact the Preludin addicts told me that for them the drug is, how you say it in America, a fock, no that's not it, a fuck pump. Yes, that's it, it's a fuck pump." Having established the correct term, he proceeded to repeat it with increasing enthusiasm. I smiled wanly and cringed a little as I noticed that the conversations at the adjoining tables had suddenly become surprisingly quiet. Undaunted, Professor Rylander detailed the sexual effects of the drug, as related to him by Preludin habitués. Their interest in sex was not only markedly stimulated, allowing them to have intercourse repeatedly over a relatively short period of time, but in addition on each occasion the orgasm was markedly delayed so that they could literally fornicate for hours at a time. This was by no means a uniform finding but was described by about 50 per cent of the heavy users.

One of the heavy users subsequently told me the following intriguing story: One year before, having heard stories of Preludin's aphrodisiac effects, he began taking the drug intravenously on weekends because he felt inadequate sexually. It was always taken in the presence of his wife and it did so markedly increase his sexual interest as well as his performance that she was far more satisfied. Six months later he persuaded her to try the drug intravenously to enhance her physical gratification. The Preludin augmented both her gratification and her desire. At first her increased sexual appetite was confined to weekends, but soon her demands on him became so great that he found he was staying home from his job in order to keep her sexually satisfied. They were both now using very large amounts of Preludin and as a consequence he became involved in criminal activity to obtain money for the drug. Finally her demands became so extraordinary that he was incapable of satisfying her and she took to leaving home and fornicating with anyone she could find who was agreeable. In Sweden, as in America, it appears not to be inordinately difficult to find such agreeable individuals. Out of work and engaged in criminal activities, the husband suffered both drug-induced and justifiable paranoia about his wife's sexual behavior pattern. One year after starting intravenous Preludin solely for pleasure, he had no job, his marriage was broken and at the time I saw him he was in jail awaiting trial for theft.

It should be emphasized that not all experts agree that the central stimulants increase heterosexual activity. Indeed, Dr. Philip Connell, England's leading authority, says that aphrodisiac effects of amphetamine drugs are psychological, not physiological; for those who want it to be a sexual stimulant, it may well be, but that it's all in the mind. Although the drugs taken intravenously appear to many people to have aphrodisiac qualities, continued heavy use results in tolerance, causing the individual to use more drugs to obtain the same effect. Such prolonged and heavy use eventually leads to sexual impotence. However, once the drug is discontinued for a short time the impotence disappears, and when the drug is again administered the aphrodisiac effects are once more noted.

With this background information, it is possible to understand more clearly the controversy of the last few years. The polemic had its beginnings in 1964, when a well-known journalist decided for himself that the punitive approach to stimulant habituation was outrageous and inhumane. In fact the punitive approach hardly exists in Sweden. If an individual is caught possessing the drug illicitly he is given a reprimand or a fine. There is no law against illicit sale, but because the drug is sold at an enormous profit on the black market, the police are able to compensate for this loophole: they can charge the indi-

vidual who sells it with profiteering, and upon conviction
he is likely to get a fine and up to six months in jail. Until
very recently, though, the laws regarding smuggling have
been astoundingly lax, the maximum penalty being two
years; this is now being increased to four years. A small
number of minor peddlers have been sentenced to as
much as two years but none of the big smugglers have
been indicted. In any case, it could hardly be claimed that
Sweden used police state tactics in regard to its treatment
of amphetamine users—and yet that is exactly what was
claimed.

A National Society for Help to Abusers of Medicines, a
private organization headed by the previously mentioned
journalist, was formed and a massive radio, television and
newspaper campaign was initiated, demanding that stimulant users be treated as sick people and insisting that the
proper treatment was maintenance therapy—that is, giving
them as much of the drug as they desired. In Sweden
there is only one television station, while in Stockholm
itself there are two morning and two afternoon newspapers. The latter two papers are popularly described as
scandal sheets. It was in these and on television that the
major part of the campaign was initiated and carried
forward. Medical policy in Sweden is determined by a
National Medical Board. Soon the attacks on the police
and the demands for a humanitarian approach compelled
the Board to form a committee on treatment of narcotics
addiction. At the present time, significantly, the secretary
of the Board is the journalist who started the whole campaign, and the secretary of the narcotics addiction subcommittee is a young lawyer entirely committed to the
maintenance concept.

In the spring of 1965 the journalist and his colleagues
had their way. The newly established narcotics addiction
subcommittee decided to embark on a great experiment
which would permit certain doctors to treat the Preludin
users with stimulants. At the same time investigations
were made into the possibility of banning Preludin entirely

and legally giving out only oral and intravenous amphetamines and oral Ritalin. In December, 1965 the use of
Preludin was indeed proscribed, but the amount available in Stockholm did not decrease. Smuggling from
Spain, France and Italy has flourished, and there continues to be a great amount of Preludin on the black
market.

It is worthwhile digressing slightly to analyze a little
more extensively the reasoning behind the maintenance
scheme. Its proponents had read two American experts;
one was Isidor Chein (*The Road to H*) and the other was
Alfred Lindesmith from Indiana, a well-known theoretical
sociologist who has formulated an interesting concept of
the genesis of opiate addiction. In their recommendations,
both Chein and Lindesmith condemned the punitive legal
approach to addiction and supported the notion that opiate addicts might do better if given their drug, thus removing the causes of criminality and permitting effective
rehabilitation.

In Sweden, the works of these two authors, neither of
whom has any personal experience with maintenance
therapy in opiate addiction, were taken as gospel. Other
writers were ignored and the Chein-Lindesmith proposals
relating to opiates were applied uncritically as public
health policy to central stimulants, an entirely different
problem. That Chein and Lindesmith had had no experience with maintenance therapy themselves appeared to
make no difference, nor did the fact that their studies
applied solely to opiates. Furthermore, the pressures for
immediate action were so great that the Swedish stimulant
maintenance program was instituted hurriedly and without
organization or caution. Funds were not appropriated for
rehabilitation, nor were proper facilities established. In
justifying the experiment to the public, the proponents
emphasized that the users were now getting their drugs
from the black market, and that if they were given their
drug by physicians it would almost surely eliminate criminality and permit them to become constructive, active

members of society. Conveniently ignored was the fact
that two-thirds of these individuals had police records
even before they started using intravenous Preludin. They
had, in addition, familial and personality problems which
virtually precluded rehabilitation merely by giving them
stimulants. Most important, the Swedish hegemony man-
aged to ignore altogether the nature of the drug they were
administering. The argument for administering methadone
or other opiates to a heroin addict is that this normalizes
the opiate-dependent addict and permits him to accept
rehabilitation, at the same time preventing him from getting any kick from supplementally administered heroin.
The rationale behind this argument is obviously valid,
even though one can readily debate the efficacy of such
programs in the United States.

But the question is whether such methods apply to the
central stimulants, such as Preludin, Methedrine and Ritalin. The answer is a resounding no. When a habituated
individual takes central stimulants intravenously, he becomes progressively more abnormal instead of normal.
The drugs result in the following toxic manifestations:
restlessness, euphoria, irritability, anxiety, tension, slurred
speech, incoordination, teeth-grinding movements, increased or irregular heart rate, dry mouth, tremor, weight
loss, headache, nausea, sleeplessness, paranoid psychoses
or a toxic confusional state. By no stretch of the imagination do these conditions constitute normalcy. And the
more drugs one gives the worse the symptoms get. And so
the great experiment, inadequately financed, hurriedly enacted with an irrational conceptual framework, started in
the spring of 1965 and continued for two years. The
results can only be described as an unmitigated disaster.

Three physicians began prescribing the drug on request,
but two soon found the situation highly unpalatable and
refused to continue, leaving one physician, Dr. B, to service the Preludin users. Even his function was limited,
because the Board of Health permitted him to have only a
certain number of patients on his roster. Eventually, over

the two year period, he handled approximately 160 patients.

I talked to him at length and found that his theory was that the drugs were a bit like chocolate. He reasoned that if people were given all the chocolate they craved they would eventually tire of chocolate. Similarly, if they were given drugs ad libitum, they would eventually tire of these drugs. This is not exactly what happened. Instead his office was inundated with habitual users of both morphine and amphetamines. Virtually no records were kept and the central-stimulant users were even allowed to make out the prescriptions themselves, which he then signed. Since the drug users were controlling the dosage, incredibly large amounts of amphetamine and Ritalin were given out; in addition, the users were given extra prescriptions if they said they had friends, wives or mistresses who desired central stimulants. These secondarily involved indivuduals were usually not seen even once by the physician. The doctor's office, even his home, became a virtual shooting gallery for intravenous stimulants. Those who were primarily addicted or habituated to morphine were given not only large amounts of that drug but also virtually as much amphetamine as they wanted. Both the amphetamines and the Ritalin were prescribed as pills or as a liquid for intravenous use. The users frequently dissolved the tablets in water and then injected the drug intravenously. A subsequent check of Dr. B's prescriptions revealed that some patients received from 400 to 500 grains of morphine monthly—hits being 24,000 to 30,000 milligrams. The enormity of this amount can be understood by relating it to the dose used in the United States by an average heroin addict: 75 to 150 milligrams per day (2,250 to 4,500 milligrams monthly).

The result of such chaotic, indiscriminate prescribing was that many of the morphine addicts rapidly became converted to simultaneous severe dependence on both amphetamines and morphine. The amphetamine-Ritalin users received so much drug that they were intoxicated virtually all the time; very few were able to maintain jobs or stable family relationships. During a one-year period, for an average of 75 patients per month, Dr. B prescribed 1.2 million milliliters of 1 per cent amphetamine, 140,000 milliliters of 1 per cent Methedrine, 158,000 milliliters of 1 per cent Ritalin (a total of about 325 gallons of intravenous stimulants), 240,000 Ritalin tablets, and 165,000 Methedrine pills. But not all the stimulants were used by the original recipients of Dr. B's largesse. The majority gave away some of the drug they legally received and sold another portion. Indeed, careful chromatographic studies in recent months suggest that some of these people were selling or giving away the majority of their personal supply. Nor was criminal behavior abolished; one-third of those who received the drug legally were apprehended for criminal activity during a 24-month period, thus destroying the argument that permissive prescribing would eliminate delinquent behavior. Additional studies showed that 25 per cent of the thousands of stimulant users in Stockholm received at least part of their drug supply either directly from the doctor or from his 160 patients.

The spread of central-stimulant abuse is well documented by the studies on individuals arrested for criminal activity. In 1965, 20 per cent of the arrested male population abused Preludin or similar drugs. In 1966, this percentage had risen to 24 per cent and by 1967 to 34 per cent. Additionally, over half the arrested women used intravenous central stimulants. Interestingly, this is almost uniformly limited to Swedish nationals and is virtually never seen among, for example, arrested Finns and Norwegians.

With free prescription and virtually uncontrolled smuggling, the number of cases of amphetamine, Ritalin and Preludin abuse was bound to increase. Indeed, the best estimates are that in 1965 when the "great experiment" started, there were some 2,000 abusers in Stockholm and that this number increased 100 per cent over the next two years.

Studies of those who use Preludin show that they are immature, lacking in goal direction, incapable of tolerating frustration, and that they almost uniformly come from either broken homes or homes in which there is no adequate father figure. Frequently, the mothers are described as overprotective. In terms of psychiatric classification the users have most often been called sociopaths or psychopaths or have been listed under the catchall term, character disorders. It is striking that the personality characteristics of the Swedish central-stimulant habitués are virtually identical to those described for heroin addicts in the United States.

Although the users were able to obtain syringes and needles legally, they had no concept of sterilization. The drug was frequently taken in communal fashion, with the sharing of needles and syringes. As one might anticipate, such patently unhygienic techniques invited hepatitis. The first case of central-stimulant-induced hepatitis was discovered in 1962 and over the next year some 130 additional cases were found. As the number of cases of stimulant abuse rose, so did the incidence of hepatitis; in 1966, there were 300 hepatitis cases and in 1967 in the first six months there were 275. The most important facet of treatment in hepatitis is bed rest. However, when the central-stimulant-induced hepatitis patients are hospitalized their craving for the drug is so great that they become major disciplinary problems. Therefore, they are now treated (for the most part) in the outpatient departments as ambulatory patients. Thus, unsterile techniques promote hepatitis, and the drug-related disciplinary problems result in the hepatitis being treated inadequately—and that is about the kindest word one can use for the outpatient treatment of overt hepatitis.

The most severe complications of excessive use of intravenous central stimulants are psychoses, which are almost always paranoid in type but which may have major confusional aspects or may occasionally mimic schizophrenia. Compulsive and/or paranoid behavior is quite characteristic of excessive stimulant use. For example, patients were described to me who took apart and put together motors or lamps for hours on end under the influence of intravenous Preludin. Women who abhor cleaning will compulsively clean a house or room over and over again for hours or even days on end. The feeling of paranoia is so great that it is an accepted part of usage and is popularly known in Sweden as "noia", a term allegedly derived by merely using the last syllable of the word paranoia. One man carried all the furniture in his house to the roof and then heaved it into the street below, screaming all the time that there were people down there waiting to kill him. Another got in his car and raced through the center of Stockholm, ignoring lights, convinced there were policemen on every corner who were waiting to kill him. Eventually, of course, the police did chase him, though they caught him only after he had smashed his automobile into a wall.

It is important to emphasize that central stimulants may produce psychosis very rapidly; psychosis has occasionally been noted within several hours after initiating intravenous use.

Of the patients treated by Doctor B, 12 to 15 per cent developed overt serious psychoses. These psychoses are usually short-lived, lasting from one to four days after discontinuing the drug. However, Professor Rylander, who has carefully studied psychoses induced by central stimulants, finds that some persist for long periods of time. The general opinion is that such individuals have disturbed personalities and that the drug merely precipitates deterioration with consequent prolonged psychosis. Professor Rylander has also analyzed a series of patients who return repeatedly to intravenous Preludin use and is convinced that a certain number have developed permanent drug-induced brain damage, a so-called organic mental syndrome. His findings thus support reports of permanent amphetamine-induced brain damage from Japan during their great stimulant epidemic of the mid-

1950s. A large percentage of the users report a loss of inhibitions. Criminal activity may be engaged in during use to obtain money or merely because the users feel far more audacious. Aggressive behavior may be marked, and thus both assaults and sexual crimes have been reported. In Sweden, however, Preludin- or Ritalin-induced violent attacks on others are relatively infrequent. Far more often the paranoia results in irrational behavior during flight from anticipated attack.

There are, of course, many stories of personal tragedy. The most poignant I heard, told me both by a psychiatrist and the patient's foster mother, appears to be irrefutably documented. A young man used hashish on occasion and in addition, during a period of two or three years, had taken a total of 50 injections of morphine. He was clearly not addicted to morphine or anything else. With a highly disorganized family background, he had an unstable personality but was able to function relatively effectively and was working. He went to Dr. B and even though he had never been addicted to anything, he was given large amounts of amphetamines. Over the subsequent months his personality deteriorated strikingly. He no longer went to work, remaining intoxicated virtually all the time. Eventually, his foster mother had him committed to a mental institution (against his will). He has now been off drugs for a year but exhibits what his foster mother, a psychiatric social worker, and doctors, interpret as an organic brain syndrome, and appears to have suffered permanent damage.

As the number of users and the number of cases of serious side effects increased, it became inevitable that somebody would launch a concerted attack on the program. This attack between 1965 and 1967 was led by my host, whom I shall call Doctor C. But each time any public opposition was voiced to the "great experiment," there was a vitriolic rejoinder in the newspapers and on radio. The opponents had no access to Swedish television and the press was entirely unsympathetic to their point of view. Understandably, the opposition became progressively more bitter. At the same time, the Board of Health became frightened, but was unwilling to admit an error that might lead to a national scandal. Repeatedly, the opponents were labeled as reactionaries, men punitively oriented and lacking any sense of humanity. Eventually Dr. C was asked by a member of the Medical Board to submit a medical report on the experiment. His report was a violent attack on the maintenance program, but it was quickly quashed. More angry still, he then submitted an article which was published in 1967 in one of the prominent Swedish medical journals. In it he noted that the incidence of psychosis was much greater among those receiving central stimulants legally than it was among those obtaining them from the black market. The conclusion was that they were getting so much more drug legally that they were experiencing greater toxic effects. In this article he directly attacked Dr. B, using bits of information on dosage and side effects that he had gathered from some fifty of Dr. B's patients. For this he was not only roundly attacked as being totally unscientific, but claims were made that he had acquired the wrong patient list.

But Dr. C, an obvious zealot, did have the correct list and in a growing rage began writing letters, public and private, to virtually everyone he could think of, attacking the experiment. His public letters were often answered by the proponents, further escalating the virulence of the controversy. Dr. C also obtained virtually all of Dr. B's back prescriptions and, by now entirely committed to a vendetta against the proponents of the scheme, he began to write a book that would expose in detailed and specific fashion the malfeasance of which he was convinced they were guilty.

By the fall of 1967 it almost seemed as if the massive and appalling central-stimulant problem in Sweden had become secondary to the personality clashes revolving around the "great experiment." In any case, the experiment was bound to fail—and fail it did with a resounding thud. In April, 1967, one of the addicts who was receiving both morphine and central stimulants gave the morphine to a young girl; she immediately died of overdose. Recognizing that there was a real scandal brewing, the Medical Board abruptly decided that Dr. B could no longer prescribe for these patients; the patients themselves were turned over to a careful academician who proceeded to reduce their doses slowly and to undertake a detailed study of the sociologic and physiologic effects of the drugs on these users.

That was the situation when I arrived. With few exceptions everyone now agreed that the problem was increasing and the experiment had been a tragic failure. The difficulty was that the personality battles had become so intense that the original proponents were in an impossible position. Their ill-conceived experiment had not worked, and with embattled, energetic, enraged Dr. C out to expose them all, even though the experiment had now been discontinued, the makings of a major political scandal existed. The instigating journalist and many others would have liked to have seen the whole episode dropped quietly while other therapeutic measures were instituted, but neither they nor the Board were willing to publicly retract their initial views on maintenance. The problem continued to rankle. Not only would it be embarrassing to have to admit publicly that they were wrong, but in addition, and I think legitimately, they feel that such an admission would undermine confidence in the Medical Board and thus in any subsequent attempts to treat the increasing drug problem on a rational and humane basis. It is obviously an unfortunate situation in which Dr. C demands and deserves vindication; but in achieving it he could do irreparable damage to the Board and to future treatment programs for drug abuse.

This then is the story in Sweden. The abuse of cannabis is growing progressively and there are beginning to be small numbers of LSD users. Their opiate problem has grown but is not serious. The central-stimulant problem—

the use of Preludin, amphetamines and Ritalin—is approaching the crisis stage, fostered by inadequate attempts to suppress the illicit traffic and the indiscriminate prescribing. Many observers feel that the peak has by no means been reached. They note that the abuse of central stimulants is spreading outside delinquent groups to involve beatniks, bohemians, the unstable, and even students with personality disorders. If this is true, then what is now regarded as a serious and growing problem may soon become a national catastrophe.

I have not revisited Sweden since 1967, but the authorities tell me the stimulant problem continues to grow. Although legal controls have been stiffened, Preludin and other stimulants are still readily available, and the current number of stimulant habitués has further increased to between 5,000 and 10,000 in Stockholm alone. Dr. C's book has indeed created a furor with charges and countercharges which will undoubtedly have to be settled by the courts. The official policy on treatment has shifted to the therapeutic community concept—group living with confrontation sessions. As with maintenance, this was adopted from the United States. The therapeutic community concept is unproved for the treatment of heroin addicts, let alone for stimulant habitués. But at least it makes more sense than maintaining a stimulant habitué on stimulants. And so it goes in Sweden.

CHAPTER SIX

THE GREAT MARIHUANA DEBATE

Fitzhugh Ludlow, a young American introduced to hashish in the mid-1850s, described his experiences as follows: "The sublime avenues and spiritual life at whose gates the soul in its ordinary state is forever blindly groping are opened wide by hashish. There is a majesty surpassing the loftiest emotions aroused by material grandeur." Hashish is, of course, similar to our marihuana but more potent. Writing of the latter substance over one hundred years later, Harry J. Anslinger, the U.S. Commissioner of Narcotics, wrote: "Much of the most irrational juvenile violence and killing that has written a new chapter of shame and tragedy is traceable directly to this hemp intoxication. A gang of boys tear the clothes from two school girls and rape the screaming girls, one boy after the other. A sixteen-year-old kills his entire family of five in Florida, a man in Minnesota puts a bullet through the head of a stranger on the road; in Colorado a husband tries to shoot his wife, kills her grandmother instead and then kills himself. Every one of these crimes had been preceeded by the smoking of one or more marihuana 'reefers.' " These views would characterize the extremes in the extraordinary marihuana polemic which has enveloped our society. Is marihuana an innocuous drug, a giver of delight, or is it intrinsically evil, leading to debauchery, degradation and criminality? It is almost ludicrous that our society, faced with so many important problems, should expend so much time, energy and intellectual endeavor on a matter as trivial as the wonders or evils of the various products derived from the inoffensive and ubiquitous plant *cannabis sativa*.

It is important to emphasize that use of marihuana is increasing markedly in the United States, although only a minority of young persons are involved. Furthermore, there is no single stereotype which could characterize these new converts to the marihuana cause; businessmen, artists, bohemians, hippies, college athletes, delinquents, honor students, alienated young people and average college or high school students all can be found in the marihuana ranks.

My own involvement in this overinflated polemic began quite innocently in the fall of 1964. I was at that time chairman of the narcotics subcommittee of the public health committee of the Medical Society of the County of New York. Our four-man subcommittee formulated a position paper, five printed pages in length, devoted primarily to background information on the problem of narcotic addiction. It included a series of fourteen recommendations, one of which stated, "The use of marihuana should not be considered equivalent to the use of opiates or cocaine, since it is not addicting. However, its use is dangerous since a significant number of marihuana users turn to addicting drugs." This hardly could be construed as a wildly liberal stand in regard to marihuana. Indeed, the only thing that should have been at all interesting about it was that it represented the first adoption by a responsible medical group of the recommendations of President Kennedy's Advisory Commission on Narcotic and Drug Abuse. In the reports of that committee in November, 1963, it was noted, "The present federal narcotics and marihuana laws equate the two drugs. Any offender whose crime is sale of a marihuana reefer is subject to the same term of imprisonment as the peddler selling heroin. In most cases the marihuana reefer is less harmful than any opiate. For one thing, while marihuana may provoke lawless behavior it does not create physical dependency. This commission makes a flat distinction between the two drugs, and believes that the unlawful sale or possession of marihuana is a less serious offense than the unlawful sale or possession of an opiate."

But much to our surprise, our own carefully worded and mild recommendation provoked more discussion, when presented both to the full membership of the medical society and to a subsequent Gracie Mansion meeting on narcotics called by Mayor Robert Wagner, than any of the other thirteen recommendations, even though some of those others represented far-reaching innovations in regard to opiate abuse. Although there was some loud dissent the position paper was adopted unanimously on January 25, 1965. A few months later, with minor modifications, these recommendations also became the official policy of the New York State Medical Society. The report was duly released at a well-attended press conference and was treated favorably by the press, both in news stories and subsequent editorials.

In March of 1966, the narcotics subcommittee formulated and promulgated a second position on the dangerous drug problem. This policy statement was directed primarily toward the abuse of LSD and similar potent hallucinogens. As its chief author, I devoted the first page to a review of the marihuana situation, against the advice of several members of the eight-man subcommittee. This position paper concluded with fifteen recommendations, one of which pertained to marihuana and said, "Marihuana should at long last be relegated to its rightful position as a mild hallucinogen, and should be removed from the opiate-cocaine category. New York State should take the lead in attempting to mitigate the stringent federal laws in regard to marihuana possession. We do not recommend changes in marihuana laws related to illicit sale or smuggling for sale." This report was also adopted by the medical society on March 28, 1966, but not without vigorous and at times highly emotional debate.

As one of the first factual reports on LSD and the first formal stand by a medical society on hallucinogenic drugs, it received wide publicity and acclaim. Many colleges reprinted it and distributed it to whole classes. It was extensively quoted both by those concerned about LSD and by those who felt that the marihuana laws were inordinately harsh. Included among those relying heavily upon it in their deliberations was President Johnson's Commission on Crime. But despite two approved position papers endorsing a moderate view, the implacable opponents of moderation persisted. In early 1967 a rumor was started that high school students were using the position papers to condone use of marihuana. Despite lack of documentation of the rumor and a continuing deluge of requests for the position paper by college administrations, the *commitia minora*, the ruling body of the medical society, voted in April, 1967, to stop its distribution. Instead, an ad hoc committee was appointed to revise the policy paper.

Well aware of the asperity of the internecine conflict, the ad hoc committee met briefly on one occasion and then was not heard from for the next five months. By that time the medical society, besieged with additional requests for the policy statement, became impatient, discharged the ad hoc committee and requested the narcotics subcommittee to update the statement. This we did with relish, without in any way changing the original stand. When the report again came before the *commitia minora* for final approval, a thirty-minute debate ensued, centering on whether the society should state that it did not condone marihuana use or whether we should specifically condemn its use. The extended argument was finally settled by acceptance of the slightly stronger term "condemn," a decision which appeared to be enormously important to the *commitia*. The vigor of the battle over insignificant differences in wording is indicative of the emotional and picayune approach to the marihuana question.

While this banal debate was going on in and about medical circles in New York, a major attempt was being made to rupture all the marihuana laws in Boston. Similar trials had taken place in Rhode Island and Oregon, but the Boston trial held in September, 1967, constituted the major confrontation. Two young men had been arrested in possession of a large amount of marihuana and were charged with possession with intent to sell. In Suffolk Superior Court in Boston, Chief Justice G. Joseph Tauro was to hear the case without jury. Attorney for the defendants was Joseph Oteri, an ebullient and articulate lawyer who argued for dismissal of the charge on the grounds that classifying possession of marihuana as a felony was cruel and unjust punishment as well as being in violation of the Constitution. For the defense, Mr. Oteri carefully mobilized virtually every authoritative sociologist, psychologist and psychiatrist in the United States who was known to be in strong disagreement with the laws regarding possession of marihuana. I was one of the first persons he approached to testify for the defense. I refused on the grounds that these young men were obviously selling marihuana and that this, therefore, was not an appropriate case; should Mr. Oteri win, he would not merely modify the laws for possession, but would sunder all marihuana laws and permit its uncontrolled distribution throughout the United States.

At the behest of Attorney James St. Clair, a superb trial lawyer employed by the state solely for the purpose of trying this case, I agreed to testify for the Commonwealth of Massachusetts. The expert medical testimony on both sides was directed to a single question: Was marihuana innocuous or was it potentially harmful? (In December, 1967, Judge Tauro rejected the defense arguments and upheld the validity of the state's marihuana statutes.) This is the crucial question. There is general agreement that marihuana characteristically produces relaxation, euphoria, giddiness, heightened perceptions, talkativeness and a mild intoxication similar in many ways to that found after ingestion of one or two shots of alcohol. But the group attempting to legalize marihuana go further and insist adamantly that it is virtually harmless; those of us who oppose legalization are as implacable in insisting that all cannabis preparations are potentially dangerous. The potential dangers, to our minds, are several.

First, there is the possibility of acute panic reaction. This is illustrated in the following 3 quotations.

"It was offered to me and I tried it. I'll tell you one thing, I never did enjoy it at all. I mean that it was just nothing that I could enjoy. Oh yes, I got definite feelings from it, but I didn't enjoy them. I mean I got plenty of reactions but they were mostly reactions of fear."

"After the first time I didn't turn on for about, I'd say, ten months to a year. It wasn't a moral thing—it was because I got so frightened being so high."

"One subject smoked one cigarette and became restless, agitated, dizzy, fearful of his surroundings and afraid of death. He had three short periods of unconsciousness."

The first two cases come from Howard Becker's article entitled, "Becoming a Marihuana User" in the *American Journal of Sociology,* and the third, surprisingly enough, is from the Mayor's Report in New York City in 1944, the report being used by the proponents of marihuana to demonstrate how innocuous the drug is. Abject fear followed by three short periods of unconsciousness surely is not the definition of an innocuous drug.

I have talked to other marihuana users who described similar panic reactions, and in recent months I have been called by several physicians reporting cases of marihuana fright observed in their own practices. It is abundantly clear that such reactions may occur after smoking a single marihuana cigarette. Perhaps the most articulate support for the notion that marihuana can produce acute panic reactions comes from, of all sources, William Burroughs, the famed author. Writing in the *British Journal of Addiction* in 1956, he said, "Marihuana is a sensitizer and the results are not always pleasant. It makes a bad situation worse. Depression becomes despair; anxiety panic. I once gave a marihuana cigarette to a guest who was mildly anxious. After smoking half a cigarette he suddenly leapt to his feet screaming, 'I got the fear,' and rushed out of the house." The evidence on panic seems so clear that to deny its existence indicates either abysmal ignorance of the facts or intentional intellectual dishonesty. At the same time, it is only fair to stress that panic reactions such as I have described are infrequent and tend to dissipate over a period of several hours once the marihuana smoking has stopped. However, there are cases on record, which appear well authenticated, in which the individual had an initial acute panic reaction followed by recurring incapacitating anxiety which persisted for a period of months. In such rare cases the toxic reactions from even a single cigarette mimic the untoward responses to potent hallucinogens such as LSD.

As Burroughs noted, marihuana can markedly exacerbate mild depression. The following is a case reported by Dr. Dana Farnsworth of Harvard University. "A nineteen-year-old man became depressed, used marihuana to combat an acute depressive episode, experienced 'black despair' and then obtained sedative pills from a friend which he took in an attempt at suicide." Dr. Martin Keeler reported similar cases in the *American Journal of Psychiatry* in November, 1967.

Acute intoxication can also occur. This syndrome, apparently synonymous to what Elizabeth Tylden, M.D., writing in the *British Medical Journal,* has called oneiric delirium, is best described in the American literature by Dr. Walter Bromberg in the *Journal of the American Medical Association* in 1939. He described fourteen patients who developed acute intoxication (often after smoking a single cigarette) characterized by excitement, mental confusion, disorientation, visual hallucinations, euphoria, hunger, talkativeness, a feeling of intellectual brilliancy, crowding of sensations, changes in time perception, recklessness lasting for several hours to several days, often accompanied by anxiety, hysterical reactions, panic states, or depressions. Some of the patients had suicidal or assaultive urges as a consequence of the acute intoxication. One patient studied by Dr. Edwin Williams and his colleagues in 1946 smoked three cigarettes and then "became greatly agitated, tore off the ear phones, wept and shouted accusations of persecution against the custodial supervisor which were definitely delusional. He protested loudly that he was innocent of all crimes and threatened anyone who would doubt it. The disturbance lasted for about an hour."

As with acute panic reactions, acute intoxication occurs only infrequently; it may supervene after smoking a single cigarette or only after the use of several cigarettes. That it can occur appears virtually incontrovertible. The only question which remains is whether acute intoxication can appear in a perfectly normal, well-adjusted person, or whether it is mandatory that the individual have substantial anxiety or personality instability. Even if one assumes that the latter is the case, it would still be clear that were the drug legalized and made available to everyone, certain persons, namely those with overt or covert personality disturbances, would incur the risk of acute intoxication as a consequence of smoking marihuana—although admittedly such a response would not often happen.

A further danger of marihuana smoking is the development of acute psychosis. In a relatively stable person a single marihuana cigarette can produce a psychosis only very rarely, but if there is substantial personality instability, marihuana, even in small amounts, occasionally precipitates one. For the most part, weak cannabis preparations such as marihuana can produce psychosis only following the use of large amounts of the drug. In Morocco, Dr. Ahmed Benabud writing in the *United Nations Bulletin on Narcotics,* reported in 1957 that 25 per cent of the male admissions to mental hospitals were diagnosed as having kif psychoses, kif being a form of cannabis similar to American marihuana. The men involved smoked kif in pipes, using 20 to 30 pipefuls each day, an enormous amount when considered in marihuana cigarette equivalents. Benabud's figures have been challenged on the grounds that the diagnosis of kif psychosis frequently was made on inadequate data and that other variables, such as co-existent malnutrition, were not thoroughly investigated.

Although some may challenge Benabud's findings, nobody has offered any serious challenge to the findings in Mayor LaGuardia's report in 1944. Using 1 to 11 standard marihuana cigarettes, or a marihuana extract equivalent to 4 to 16 cigarettes, the investigators found that 9 out of 77 persons developed acute psychotic episodes. These findings have been confirmed by Dr. Harris Isbell of the University of Kentucky. Using a purified form of the active principle of marihuana, tetrahydrocannabinol, he is able to show that if he gives a dose of 50 micrograms per kilogram of body weight, most subjects experience altered time sense and more vivid visual and auditory perceptions. When the dose was increased to over 200 micrograms, a large dose, all subjects underwent some psychotic reactions including illusions, delusions and hallucinations. One of his patients became catatonic and mute for several hours. Dr. T. Asuni, reporting in the *United Nations Bulletin on Narcotics* in 1964, recorded 37 cases in two hospitals in Nigeria of toxic cannabis psychosis characterized by auditory hallucinations, paranoia, and thought disorders which appeared similar to schizophrenia. In many of these there was no prior history of mental disease and although most recovered within a period of three months, some had a prolonged period of incapacitation. Tylden describes an intriguing case of a sixteen-year-old boy who had smoked for three years. During that entire period he appeared schizophrenic, but as soon as he stopped smoking cannabis, and apparently without other therapeutic endeavors, the symptoms of disorder faded and he began to work steadily. Three reports of acute mental breaks after use of marihuana requiring psychiatric treatment or hospitalization appeared in American medical journals in 1969. Summarizing these studies, it would be fair to say that cannabis psychosis is in general a dose-related phenomenon. Even one marihuana cigarette in an unstable personality can on occasion precipitate a psychosis, but for the most part psychosis is associated either with utilization of very large amounts over a short period of time or with chronic heavy use. The marihuana proponents can justifiably claim that if one smokes only one or two cigarettes a day of American type marihuana, psychotic reactions are rare. But for the heavy user, or the pothead, who smokes almost constantly, the story is entirely different. Once precipitated, the psychosis usually improves in a period of several days to several months after marihuana use is stopped, but it is clear that on occasion it can last for a very long time.

Another complication, which has been underemphasized but is now being reported with increasing frequency, is marihuana-induced loss of goals and ambition. The following is a case of Farnsworth's.

"A senior premedical student with an excellent academic record, already admitted to a medical school, suddenly began to do failing work in one course. He said his energies had been diverted into trying to stop using marihuana which he had begun using extensively during his senior year. When faced with the necessity of studying he found it easier to 'take pot.' Under its influence he was convinced that studying for examinations was not as important as other things. He wanted help, stating explicitly that he considered the use of marihuana harmful because it encouraged him as well as his friends who used it to 'evade reality and pursue illusory goals.'"

A more mundane but possibly even more serious danger results from the effect of marihuana on coordination and the performance of motor acts. Tests show that simple motor acts are performed normally under the influence of marihuana, but that complex ones are clearly impaired. Skilled motor acts are performed more rapidly, but less accurately; furthermore, marihuana distorts time and space perception. Obviously, then, those driving an automobile under the influence of marihuana are potentially dangerous to themselves and to others. Thus far, despite anecdotal reports, there are no statistical data linking marihuana to automobile accidents. Of course, thousands of people die each year in this country because of automobile accidents caused by persons under the influence of alcohol. The question is whether we want to add to the millions of people who now drink and drive, additional millions who would smoke marihuana and then drive while intoxicated from this drug. To my mind, we already have enough problems with accidents caused by one intoxicant without adding another. At least with alcohol, scientific methods are available to measure blood alcohol levels, permitting at least some punishment to be meted out to those who are driving under the influence. With marihuana, there are currently no adequate methods for measuring the drug either in blood or urine. Consequently, the only way of detecting usage of the drug is by observing the presence of a typical odor on the person's breath or the presence of whole or partially consumed marihuana cigarettes in the car or on the individual's person. Then it is possible to ask him whether or not he was smoking marihuana, but if he says no, there is no way to prove he was under the drug's influence. Under such conditions, the thought of legalizing the drug and inflicting marihuana-intoxicated drivers on the public seems abhorrent.

With marihuana and other cannabis preparations, the dosage phenomenon is of prime importance. The pothead is equivalent to the alcoholic. He does not take the drug only intermittently or even daily in small doses, but attempts to remain intoxicated as much of the time as possible. For the pothead the drug is clearly dangerous. He incurs a substantial risk of personality deterioration or even the precipitation of a sub-acute or chronic psychosis. Furthermore, the drug becomes the center of his life and, as with some LSD users, he withdraws from society into a drug cocoon. A current estimate is that 1-5 per cent of those who use marihuana on more than several occasions will become potheads.

Marihuana users become potheads in part because of personality defects and in part because youth is characterized by an immoderation which often prevents drug users from adhering to sensible dosage limits. Most important, it is very difficult for the novice experiencing marihuana for the first time to predict whether he will be an occasional user, will become heavily involved or will become a pothead.

Hashish, the pure resin from the hemp plants, is five to eight times as potent as American marihuana. Used extensively in England but far less in the United States, it produces panic, acute intoxication and acute psychosis far more frequently than does our form of marihuana. I talked to patients in England who use hashish almost exclusively and they described delusions, hallucinations and illusions under the influence of hashish which are indistinguishable from those described by LSD users. In some, the precipitated psychosis was severe enough to require a substantial period of hospitalization. The medical literature from India, Greece and England is replete with descriptions of psychoses induced by the more potent forms of cannabis. For example, in the *British Medical Journal in* 1967, Dr. Peter Dally recorded the case of a ninteen-year-old boy who smoked a large reefer and thereafter developed anxiety and panic. "Four months later in spite of psychiatric treatment he still experiences severe anxiety and unreality and has frightening hypnagogic hallucinations." In the same report Dally refers to a twenty-four-year-old man with a law degree who, under the influence of hashish, decided that he could conquer time by releasing cerebral pressure. To this end, he drilled a hole into, but not through, his skull. Even the most avid proponents of pot would be unlikely to consider this as rational behavior. Tylden describes a sixteen-year-old pregnant girl who, after one hashish cigarette, had terrifying nightmares and was semiconscious the whole next day. In India, I. C. Chopra and R. N. Chopra collected 600 cases of acute confusional insanity, mania or melancholia ascribed primarily to the effects of hashish or ganga. In 200 of the 600 there was a primary underlying psychiatric disorder which appeared to have been exacerbated by cannabis, but in the other 400 the cannabis was the only cause of the insanity. If we were to legalize marihuana it would be virtually impossible not to similarly condone the use of hashish which is, after all, the same drug in purer form, but substantially more dangerous.

These several major points appear to me to illustrate convincingly that marihuana is not an innocuous drug. Three other points deserve brief mention. First, is marihuana addicting? The answer is unequivocally no, at least if one defines addiction as physical dependence. Among persons who smoke marihuana and then stop, there may be, however, enormous craving for the drug (psychological dependence) just as there may be for cigarettes in one who has been a heavy smoker. Repeatedly it is implied that since marihuana is not addicting, it is not dangerous. This is intermixing two disparate issues. Marihuana may not be addicting but it is potentially dangerous.

Second, does marihuana lead to violence? Despite lurid stories in the press, almost all of them from a decade ago or so, there is no statistical evidence associating marihuana with violence in the United States, although there are occasional anecdotal reports which are relatively convincing. In India, the Chopras found that 1 to 2 per cent of criminal cases, including murders, could be ascribed to temporary or permanent cannabis derangement. In the *British Medical Journal* recently, cases of violence in Indians smoking hemp were also described. It would be fair to say that for the most part marihuana increases passivity, not aggression, but it does release inhibitions, it can produce panic or confusion and because of these effects can on occasion indeed lead to aggressive or violent behavior.

Third, does marihuana lead to the use of other drugs such as heroin or LSD? The evidence on this appears quite clear. The overwhelming majority of some 200 million users of cannabis in the world never go on to other drugs. However, the overwhelming majority of heroin and/or LSD users in both the United States and England have had prior experience with either marihuana or hashish. There is nothing about marihuana which compels an individual to become involved with other more potent drugs. Marihuana use, however, is often an individual's initiation into the world of illicit drug use. Having entered that world—having broken the law—he may then become immersed in the drug sub-culture and in sequential form progress to abuse of a variety of other drugs including LSD, amphetamines and heroin. If the individual lives in a ghetto area of a large urban center, his use of marihuana has not only put him outside the confines of the law, but also may have cemented a relationship between him and a delinquent peer group in which the natural progression has been from marihuana to heroin and he, of course, may follow suit. In middle or upper socio-economic groups marihuana is much more likely to lead the user to the abuse of LSD. There are two reasons for this. One is that the same people in the college or social sub-group who are pushing marihuana are also likely to be prose-lytizing the use of LSD. The other is that the high for marihuana is in miniature form like the reaction to LSD. If the individual enjoys the marihuana experience and revels in his intoxication, it is not unlikely that, influenced by availability and the great amount of publicity, he will turn to a much greater kick of the same general type— namely, potent hallucinogens such as LSD. Indeed, 1966 and 1967 statistics on marihuana and LSD use from several colleges suggest that 10-45 per cent of those who started with marihuana subsequently used LSD. Additional studies in 1968-1969 show similar results.

Marihuana does not in any way mandate use of other drugs, but it may be the beginning of the road at the end of which lies either LSD or heroin. Conversely, it appears entirely reasonable to assume that if certain individuals, although the percentage is not known, did not begin with marihuana they would never get around to using the more potent and dangerous drugs.

In summary, cannabis is not an innocuous drug, as some have claimed. Granted that marihuana if smoked in moderation will not harm the overwhelming majority of people who use it, granted that it is far less dangerous than heroin or LSD, there are still compelling reasons for not permitting its legalization. Those who would legalize it would do so because they believe it is ordinarily harmless and because it is their particular intoxicant of choice. The arguments for restricted or unrestricted use are now based predominantly on hedonism. It seems to me that in an already drugged and intoxicated society, we should be extraordinarily cautious, even reluctant and negativistic, about adding any new inebriant unless that drug is truly innocuous; and the evidence on cannabis indicates that it is potentially a dangerous drug, especially if large amounts or more potent forms are used. And for those who are 8-16 and smoke marihuana, thinking difficulties may occur on one cigarette a day.

It has been suggested that in addition to providing a pleasant experience, marihuana has beneficial effects on the user. It allegedly augments creativity, but there are no valid data in support of this contention. On a substantial number of occasions creative people have deliberately been given marihuana and asked to carry out and interpret their artistic activity under the drug's influence. In the majority of cases, during the actual period of marihuana intoxication they felt that their creative activities were enhanced. However, almost uniformly, when the effects of the marihuana had dissipated and they again viewed their creative activities, they found that in actuality they had done very badly, a judgment substantiated by impartial observers. Although there is no evidence that creative performance is improved, it does appear true that in some persons marihuana may augment aesthetic sensitivity. It is perfectly clear, however, that for most people there is no true increase in aesthetic sensitivity under the influence of the drug and that in general such effects, if valid, would be limited to those who would ordinarily score high on tests designed to measure aesthetic appreciation, such as artists, musicians, etc.

More recently for instance, it has been suggested by Dr. Joel Fort, an important witness at the Boston marihuana trial, that marihuana has specific medical uses. Medicinal uses for cannabis have been claimed since approximately 3000 B.C. At that time the Chinese Emperor Shen Nung recommended treatment with the hemp plant for female weakness, gout, rheumatism, malaria, beriberi, constipation and absentmindedness. For centuries cannabis was used in folk medicine in India. There it was prescribed to stimulate the libido, for insomnia, nervous irritability, constipation, dyspepsia, dysmenorrhea, diarrhea, headache and neuralgia, in cases of tetanus, asthma, whooping cough, convulsions, strychnine poisoning, delirium tremens, and gonorrhea, for relief of migraine and pains, during labor, and as a poultice on piles. There were over twenty cannabis preparations in India which were given specifically for aphrodisiac purposes. To illustrate how confused folk medicine was, it should be pointed out that in addition to the twenty aphrodisiac preparations of cannabis there were six aphrodisiac preparations whose major component was opium, a drug acknowledged to be one of the most potent of sexual depressants. Regarding marihuana, there is not one whit of evidence to show that it is an aphrodisiac. It may reduce sexual inhibitions and thus increase sexual activity, but more likely, by increasing passivity and concentration on the drug experience, it will reduce sexual interest and activity. There are said to have been over one hundred articles on the medicinal value of cannabis published between 1840 and 1900. But gradually it became clear that cannabis was ineffective in most of the conditions for which it was being used, and, more recently, the discovery of new and more predictable agents has eliminated marihuana or any other form of cannabis as a useful drug in the treatment of human disease. As a matter of fact, those who suggest that marihuana in its present form might be beneficial medically are limited for evidence to a tiny number of reports in the medical literature, either giving preliminary data on cannabis-like drugs or anecdotal descriptions of single cases. The last such report appeared several years ago. In 1964 the prestigious *British Medical Journal* concluded that there were no valid medical uses for cannabis. To suggest that a drug—which has been used in folk medicine for over five thousand years but is now being replaced as ineffective even there—should suddenly be introduced into sophisticated Western medicine without careful additional experimentation, is patently ridiculous. Now that the active principle, the tetrahydrocannabinols, can be readily synthesized, such experimentation can be performed, but on the basis of past data there is little reason to believe that cannabis preparations will play any significant role in medical therapeutics in the future.

Inevitably, into the diatribe over marihuana has crept a comparison between marihuana and alcohol. The proponents for legalization of marihuana not only demand the comparison be made but insistently point out that alcohol is a dangerous drug which is perfectly legal in our society. They say, "If you drink alcohol, a dangerous drug, for your pleasure, why shouldn't we who dislike alcohol smoke marihuana for our pleasure, since marihuana is clearly no more dangerous than alcohol." To argue for marihuana on the grounds that it is no more dangerous than alcohol is, of course, a totally negative approach. The marihuana comparison was given substantial impetus in October, 1967, when Dr. James Goddard, Commissioner of the Food and Drug Administration, said, "Whether or not marihuana is a more dangerous drug than alcohol is debatable. I don't happen to think that it is." That statement surely was not considered particularly portentous by Dr. Goddard, but it was treated by the press as if it were an apocalyptical pronouncement, and was even accorded headlines on the front page of the conservative *New York Times*. It seems to me that the comparison is both unfortunate and irrelevant and should be avoided. Surely alcohol itself is a dangerous drug. Indeed, marihuana's dangers, both in regard to psychic damage and potential hazards for those driving under the influence, seem no greater than the documented deleterious effects of alcohol. If the question before us were a national referendum to decide whether we would use for one of our legitimate escape mechanisms either alcohol or marihuana, I might personally vote for marihuana—but that is not the question. The question is simply whether we are to add to our alcohol burden another intoxicant. In the United States there is currently a death from automobile accidents approximately every eleven minutes and an injury every eighteen seconds. Shall we add another intoxicant such as marihuana, increase the number of inebriated drivers or pedestrians and attain a death rate of perhaps one every eight minutes or even every five minutes and an injury every twelve seconds or every eight seconds? Surely society must have the right, indeed the obligation, to control its escape mechanisms and intoxicants.

Those who would legalize marihuana prefer to keep the debate parochial, limiting the arguments to marihuana's dangers, its pleasures and a comparison with alcohol. It isn't that simple. The legalize-marihuana controversy must be viewed within the broad perspective of possible legitimatization of a whole raft of potentially harmful drugs, with pleasure-giving capabilities. If we are to legalize marihuana, why stop there? Increasing numbers of people are now using central stimulants such as the amphetamines. Two amphetamine pills taken daily are surely no more dangerous than the chronic moderate use of alcohol. Shall we then legitimatize amphetamines as well as marihuana, on the grounds that many people like the kick from these drugs more than they do the kick from either alcohol or marihuana? Clearly the line must be drawn somewhere, or else, as our pharmacological cornucopia provides us with an increasing number of hallucinogens, euphoriants and stimulants, we will be so burdened with intoxicants that inevitably we will reach a stage at which society cannot function. Most people would accept that premise, but there is sharp disagreement as to where we should draw the line. My own conviction is that we are already a drugged society with ample escape mechanisms in caffeine, tobacco and alcohol and that the addition of marihuana is not only unnecessary but would open the floodgates to a farrago of drugs used primarily for hedonistic purposes.

If, then, one accepts that marihuana and other forms of cannabis are not entirely harmless, and that legalization would be unwise for our society at this time, the remaining question is whether our current legal structure in regard to this drug makes sense? It seems to me that our laws in regard to marihuana represent an appalling anachronism. The drug, after all, has limited dangers, does not necessarily lead to other drugs, and does not ordinarily provoke violence: its use must be regarded as a peccadillo, not a major crime. Yet we continue to insist on treating it as if it were a heinous offense. At the federal level, conviction for possession carries a two-year minimum sentence whereas, for example, there was as of May, 1968, no penalty for possession of LSD, a much more potent drug in the same general hallucinogenic class. Currently, possession of LSD has been made a misdemeanor with a maximum penalty of one year in jail. A second-possession offense at the federal level incurs a minimum sentence of five years. The maximum sentence for first-offense possession is ten years, and for the second offense up to twenty years. In New York State, where the laws are ordinarily quite reasonable, there is now no mandatory minimum penalty for any crime. Although mandatory minimums are theoretically abolished, if an individual is convicted on a felony charge (such as possession of more than twenty-five marihuana cigarettes) and if he is then sentenced to incarceration in a state jail, he must serve a minimum period of at least one year. For possession of twenty-five or more marihuana cigarettes there is a maximum sentence of seven years and this increases to a maximum of fifteen years for possession of over one hundred cigarettes. On the other hand, possession of LSD carries a one-year maximum sentence and sale of LSD a seven-year maximum sentence. Thus, as with the federal law, marihuana is treated more severely than the potent and dangerous LSD. In California, conviction on a possession charge can result in a sentence of one to ten years in state prison, whereas conviction for possession of LSD results in penalties of up to one year in the county jail and/or a $1,000 fine.

Three points should be made about the marihuana laws. First, in the overwhelming majority of states, just as in federal law, there is no distinction made between heroin and marihuana—or if there is a distinction it is an extremely minor one. This situation has existed since 1937, when marihuana was included in the narcotic laws, although it is neither a narcotic nor addicting.

Second, there have been some instances of patently outrageous sentences either for use of marihuana or for possession of relatively small amounts. One of the most celebrated is a Texas case of a woman of dubious reputation who, for the possession of a small amount of marihuana, was given an incredible fifteen-year sentence. She has subsequently been released, but not before serving a substantial period of time in jail. In Indianapolis, a seventeen-year-old boy was sentenced to four years in a school for delinquents for possession of marihuana, and in New York State a young man arrested for possession of marihuana has his bail set at $35,000. Timothy Leary's thirty-year sentence for marihuana transport was fortunately overturned by the Supreme Court, but in Texas he was again sentenced in March, 1970 to ten years in prison. That is absolutely appalling. I, of course, stand as no advocate for Timothy Leary, but surely it must be evident even to some bureaucratic nitwit that although Leary is a user of many drugs and a proselytizer, he is not a venal purveyor. It is certainly true that he has inflicted on society a great deal of turmoil and even damage by inveigling young people into taking dangerous drugs, but these activities in no way justify the outrageous sentence in this case. Even under our present outmoded and unjust laws in regard to marihuana he should have been charged with possession, not transport, and been given a two-year sentence with careful consideration of suspension, probation or parole. Our laws are so bad that in some states people have been and are now being put in jail for merely being in a house in which marihuana is either present or is being used; in Massachusetts for example, this so-called offense can result in a maximum five-year sentence, whereas in California the punishment for visiting a place where marihuana is being dispensed is a maximum of one year in a county jail or up to ten years in state prison.

Third, it is important to realize that despite the cases I have cited, there are very few people serving jail sentences of more than one year in the United States for possession of small amounts of marihuana intended for their own use. Mr. Oteri, the Boston lawyer, chose as his test case one involving possession of large amounts of marihuana with obvious intent to sell because, according to his own admission, he could not find a satisfactory one to appeal in which a severe sentence had been imposed in Massachusetts for mere possession of small amounts. In New York State an inquiry to the district attorney of the County of New York reveals that no accurate statistics have been kept, but it is estimated that 60 to 70 per cent of the marihuana felonies are reduced to misdemeanors. This means that even those possessing large amounts of marihuana are for the most part being sentenced under the misdemeanor laws with a maximum penalty of one year. According to the district attorney's office, "In the last year and one-half I know of no cases where defendants were sent to jail in cases that involved small amounts of marihuana." Since the district attorney's office handles primarily cases in which a large amount has been found on the individual, further inquiry was made at the criminal courts. There, it is clear that defendants are sent to jail for possession of small amounts of marihuana but not for periods of more than a year. If a defendant has no prior record, the sentence is almost invariably suspended and the defendant placed on probation. If he does have a prior record, and is convicted, there is a mandatory minimum sentence of six months and that is usually what is imposed. These findings are supported by discussions with law enforcement officials across the state. It thus would seem that in New York State a small number of marihuana users are indeed being sent to jail, but then only for a period of several months. It is thus clear that although the laws are inordinately harsh and unfair in their penalty provisions, law enforcement officials and the judiciary take these inequities into consideration in the prosecution and sentencing of those arrested for mere possession of marihuana. However, this is not always so; in three 1968-1969 cases, 9-25 years were given for mere possession.

The middle road makes the most sense in this debate: do not legalize or condone marihuana or change the penalties for sale and smuggling in transport, but do mitigate the penalties in regard to possession so that a minor crime is punished by a minor sentence, and eliminate any penalty for merely being in a place where marihuana is used. This moderate approach is, of course, acerbically rejected by both extremes. Those who would retain stringent penalties for possession either feel, usually without much justification, that marihuana is synonymous with moral turpitude or believe that it inevitably leads to use of stronger agents. The latter is the more prevalent argument, the assumption being made that a strict sentence will prevent the user from subsequent abuse of more dangerous drugs such as LSD or heroin. This, of course, means that the individual user is being punished not so much for what he did, but for what he might do in the future, an approach which is totally inconsistent with the legal principles guiding our democratic form of government. The other extreme, represented by the National Student Association, as well as by a small number of physicians, psychologists and sociologists, would have all penalties for possession of marihuana removed. This, the so-called liberal position, makes the basic assumption that any drug, including marihuana or LSD, taken by an individual for his own pleasure, is his business and nobody else's. The facile liberal view obviously has great appeal for a substantial number of high school and college students, an increasing number of whom experiment with marihuana.

If society removes all penalties for possession of marihuana it merely encourages use. As applied to hashish and pure tetrahydrocannabinol, the liberal view would augment use of forms of cannabis with far more potential for harm. Furthermore, if the drug is to remain illegal, it seems incongruous and unfair to punish the purveyor but not the buyer who encourages and supports the seller's criminal activities.

There are those who say legal sanctions never have and never will be effective in reducing drug usage. This is not so. A comparable situation occurred in Japan in the 1950s when amphetamine abuse became epidemic. The Japanese passed laws making illicit possession punishable by up to five years in prison and sale punishable by up to seven years in jail. These laws, as well as control of supply and a massive educational effort, promptly stopped the epidemic. There are many other instances which could be adduced demonstrating control of drug abuse by vigorous legal sanctions.

CHAPTER SEVEN

LSD: DISCOVERY, INVESTIGATION
AND ASCENDANCY

LSD was synthesized initially in 1938, but it was not until five years later, in 1943, that Dr. Albert Hofmann discovered the drug's hallucinogenic potential. In April of that year he inadvertently either inhaled or ingested LSD and then noted, "I felt strangely restless and dizzy. I lay down and sank into a not unpleasant delirium which was marked by an extreme degree of phantasy. In a sort of trance with closed eyes fantastic visions of extraordinary vividness accompanied by a kaleidoscopic play of intense coloration continuously swirled around me. After two hours this condition subsided." With characteristic acumen, Hofmann assumed that the hallucinogenic reaction was due to the LSD he had synthesized years before, and in order to document this irrefutably, he intentionally took 250 micrograms of the material and experienced phantasies which were similar to but even more intense than before. Since Hofmann's remarkable discovery, an enormous amount of work has been carried out on LSD. It seems reasonable to divide the LSD story into two parts, the first concentrating on the historical background of the psychedelic movement, the properties of LSD, its potential uses and increasing popularity, which in many ways reached an apogee in mid-1966. Then, in the next chapter, I shall concentrate on abuse of LSD, disillusionment with it and the growing data on its enormous potential dangers. Actually the positive and negative aspects of

LSD overlap chronologically, but in terms of organization and ease of understanding it seems reasonable to make this kind of arbitrary division.

The search for escapism and euphoria can be traced back thousands of years. In many societies, the use of drugs has held an honorable place, and so it does even today in some parts of the world. The use of LSD in the United States can perhaps be put into clearer perspective by briefly examining drug use among some of the primitive tribes.

Peyote is a small spineless cactus which grows in Mexico and the southwestern United States. Most of the cactus lies beneath the ground; the part which protrudes above ground, the so-called button, is cut off and dried. Then several of the dried buttons, which have a bitter, unpleasant taste, are ingested. The hallucinations begin to appear one to one and one-half hours later and last for several hours. First used among Mexican Indians, peyote was introduced into the United States shortly after the Civil War, and thereafter its use spread rapidly among the American Plains Indians. Then, as now, it was used in the course of a highly organized religious ritual as an aid in the expiation of sins, in making requests of the gods, in contacting and gaining the approbation of higher spirits, or in the resolving of personal conflicts. Used intermittently under rather rigidly controlled circumstances, peyote has allegedly produced relatively few adverse reactions, and the Indians using it appear for the most part to have acquired from it peace of mind, wisdom and strength of purpose. Indeed, a formal religion, The Native American Church, has grown around it and for the 200,000 members of that organization, the peyote ritual is both important and legal. But outside the aegis of the Native American Church peyote has been proscribed in many states. The active principle of peyote is the alkaloid mescaline, synthesized in 1926. Modern literature abounds with flamboyant descriptions of beautiful visual hallucinations experienced under the influence of the drug, the best known writings being those of Havelock Ellis in 1896 and of Aldous Huxley in the 1950s.

Fly agaric is derived from the mushroom *Amanita muscaria,* which is highly prized in the barren and formidable areas of the northeastern regions of Asia, where three Siberian tribes, the Koryak, Chuckchee and Kamchadal, make use of the hallucinogenic properties of the mushroom for simple pleasure, as an escape from their harsh environment, as well as to facilitate contact with spirits. The mushroom, which is often hard to come by, is dried and strung up in threes, this being the average dose. The dry mushrooms are torn into small shreds and chewed, piece by piece, then swallowed with a little water. Among the Koryaks, dutiful wives chew the mushroom, which has an unpleasant taste, and then offer the ready quid for their husbands to swallow. Shortly thereafter the first phase of the intoxication occurs, characterized by excitement, increased physical strength, agility and euphoria. For example, one man described how he would lay aside his snow shoes and walk through the deep snow hour after hour by the side of his dogs for the mere pleasure of arduous exercise and would have no feeling of fatigue. Others sing, dance and develop characteristic facial twitches. A second state, characterized by auditory hallucinations and visualization of spirits, follows. The spirits speak directly to the intoxicated person and he or she will answer out loud, carrying on prolonged and frequently animated conversations. During this stage objects appear to increase strikingly in size so that, for example, an individual picking up a small knife will grasp the handle with both hands, as if it were enormous. The third stage is the wildest. The individual is unconscious of his surroundings, but is active, walking, tumbling on the ground, raving and breaking things. Then he falls into a heavy slumber. Upon awakening, he may have pronounced hangover, marked nausea, vomiting and headache. Perhaps the most important aspect of mushroom ingestion among these poverty-stricken people is the intensity of their communion with spirits. Tribesmen give great obeisance to these spirits and obey their commands, no matter how bizarre. One man, for example, about to retire after ingesting the mushroom, was ordered by the spirits to lie down with his dog team, which he insisted on doing even though the dogs attacked him and bit him severely.

There is an additional intriguing facet to the use of fly agaric in Siberia. As noted above, the mushroom, although revered, is frequently difficult to obtain, especially for the more improvident members of the community. In some arcane fashion, fly agaric users discovered that to drink the urine of one who has recently eaten fly agaric produces the same effect as the mushroom itself. Evincing the infinite adaptability of man, the poorer members of the tribes, when the mushroom is not readily available to them, will collect the urine of their social betters after the latter have ingested fly agaric and, their passion for intoxication overcoming any natural compunctions, will pass it around in ordinary tea cups. It would seem fairly safe to predict that this is one hallucinogenic fad not likely to become popular in the United States.

In Australia certain of the aborigines who live a nomadic life in barren areas without adequate amounts of either food or water, have adapted to their cruel environment in two ways. First, their kidneys are able to concentrate urine to a phenomenal degree, thus conserving water, and second, they use pituri, the most active principle of which is scopolamine, a substance used in pure form to produce twilight sleep during childbirth. The leaves of the potato-like shrub from which the drug is derived are collected, dried, roasted, moistened and mixed with ashes from burned acacia wood. This mixture, somewhat irritating to the mouth, is then chewed, following which the nomads forget their hunger and thirst and are able to travel great distances without either food or water.

In Latin America, especially in Venezuela, Brazil and Colombia, primitive tribes either snuff or drink substances known variously as *yakee, epena, vinho de jurumena, yopo* and *niopo,* which generally contain the potent hallucinogen dimethyltryptamine. Depending on the tribe, these are used for religious purposes, magic, orgies or as a prelude to warfare. Some of the tribes using these agents, such as the Yanomamö Indians of Venezuela and Brazil, are extraordinarily fierce and treacherous. According to Richard Schultes, who has made the most exhaustive study of these substances, "The witch doctors see visions in color. The large dose used by the witch doctor is enough to put him into a deep but disturbed sleep during which he sees visions and has dreams which, through the wild shouts emitted in his delirium, are interpreted by an assistant. That it is a dangerous practice is acknowledged by the witch doctors themselves. They report the death of one of their numbers from the Puinave tribe during *yakee-*intoxication." As practiced today in the Orinoco basin of Colombia and Venezuela *yopo*-sniffing is a dangerous habit carried on not by witch doctors alone but by the whole population—men, women and children. The frightening intoxication first produces convulsive movements and distortions of the face and body muscles, then a desire to dance which is rapidly overwhelmed by an inability to control the limbs; it is at this point that a violent madness or deep sleep disturbed by a nightmare of frightening sights takes over. The intoxication always ends in a long stupor."

The ancient Incas used a solanaceous plant of the *datura* group whose pulverized seeds contained hallucinogens including scopolamine and hyoscyamine. The South American Chibchas anciently gave women and slaves *datura* to induce stupor prior to their being buried alive with departed husbands or masters. Today in rural parts of Mexico as well as in primitive areas of Ecuador, Peru and Colombia, *datura* preparations are still used. According to

Schultes, "many South American Indians thus bring on the intoxication which is marked by an initial state of violence so furious that the partaker must be held down pending the arrival of the deep disturbed sleep during which visual hallucinations interpreted as spirit visitations are experienced. This narcosis enables the witch doctor to diagnose diseases, to discover thieves and to prophesy the outcome of tribal affairs and hopes."

Among natives of certain areas of Asia, Africa and Latin America, vines or plants containing the alkaloids harmaline and harmine are used for their striking hallucinogenic properties. In Africa the alkaloids are used frequently as a stimulant or in ordeal ceremonies, whereas in Latin America it is taken in the form of a drink and used for purposes of prophecy, in social affairs, to fortify the bravery of their young men and as an aphrodisiac. It also plays a major role in the cruel *yurupara* whipping ceremony in which young men, as part of the rites of manhood, lash each other with whips until they are covered with bloody welts and fall into a drug-induced slumber. After the drink is taken, striking gastro-intestinal distress ensues and almost invariably the drinker vomits. Subsequently, he has colored, usually pleasant visual hallucinations, but thereafter, especially if the dose is excessive, the visions may become garish and frightening.

In Mexico, the morning-glory plant and the mushroom *Psilocybe mexicana* (the former called *ololiuqui*, and the latter, *teonanacatl*), provide hallucinogenic escape. A consumption of ten to twelve *teonanacatl* mushrooms produces muscular incoordination followed by a feeling of well-being and pleasure, and these feelings are accompanied by extraordinarily vivid three-dimensional visions. The visions may be amazingly detailed, projecting, for example, a formal ball in a magnificent palace. Extreme hilarity is characteristic of the early phases of Psilocybe intoxication, followed by the hallucinations and then usually by deep sleep. The use of the sacred mushroom is by no means a new phenomenon in Mexico. It can be traced to approximately 1500 B.C. The Aztecs, who apparently had catholic tastes in hallucinogenic drugs, used what appears to be *Psilocybe mexicana* for a variety of reasons, including religious ceremonies, rituals, orgies and for pure hedonism. The following is a description of Aztec mushroom use taken from an article by Dr. Francisco Guerra in the *British Journal of Addiction*, March, 1967, "They had another method of getting drunk which made them more cruel. This was by means of some small mushrooms that grow in these lands. The consumers would see a thousand visions, particularly snakes, and as they lost their senses it would seem to them that their legs and body were filled with maggots which ate them alive, and in this state, half-mad, they would go out of doors begging someone to kill them, and in this condition of intoxication it sometimes happened that they choked and also that they became very cruel to other people." In addition, it is known that mushroom-consuming ceremonies also took place after bloody ritualistic sacrifices.

Thus it is the world over, perhaps since civilization began. For the most part, the hallucinogenic search for relief from the real or imagined travails of an oppressive environment, for fortitude, for communication with spirits, for apocalyptic revelations, is carried out by primitive peoples in rather rigidly structured circumstances. Even when used for orgiastic, aphrodisiac or purely hedonistic purposes, the drugs have been utilized within the accepted mores of the group or society. Such uses are far different from what has happened in connection with LSD in the affluent United States, where a small group of individuals utilize potent hallucinogens as a symbol of rebellion against, and as a mechanism for withdrawal from, the established laws and mores.

The circumstances surrounding the use of these drugs in our sophisticated, urbanized Western society are so different from the use of hallucinogens in primitive societies over the centuries that they must be considered representative of entirely disparate phenomena.

LSD is a remarkable drug. Since its discovery in 1943, over two thousand articles have appeared in medical literature analyzing its effects in man and experimental animals. When given to cats it makes them afraid of mice; spiders, which normally weave delicately shaped webs, under the influence of LSD weave irregular smaller ones with badly spaced patterns. The Siamese fighting fish, under LSD, will maintain a nose up, vertical position and swim backwards. In rabbits and rats LSD produces fever, whereas in the pigeon profound hypothermia occurs—it changes body carbohydrate metabolism, stimulates the pituitary gland at the base of the brain and increases the amount of circulating adrenalin. Pigeons given the drug become withdrawn and catatonic, whereas dogs often show excitement. In several animal species the drug strikingly reduces the amount of inflammation found after exposure to certain foreign proteins.

LSD is a potent antagonist of serotonin, a normally occurring neurohumor thought to be vital in the proper functioning of the nervous system. For a long time it was thought that this interference with serotonin was responsible for the hallucinations induced by the drug. However, other substances chemically similar to LSD interfere equally with serotonin and yet do not produce hallucinations. More recently, it was shown that after LSD penetrated into brain cells, the serotonin content of these cells rose, an occurrence concomitant with behavioral changes. It was, therefore, felt possible that LSD acted not by affecting the amount of circulating extra-cellular serotonin but rather by changing the content within the cells. Despite these studies, there is at present no incontrovertible evidence that the drug acts by its capacity to interfere with serotonin.

Given to guppy fish, LSD directly stimulates the pigment-forming cells of the skin, causing a darkening in color. In man urine formation is diminished under the drug's influence. In monkeys LSD produces visual disturbances, blindness and incoordination. Interestingly, in several animal species it causes an increase in aggressive behavior. Learning skills in both man and animals ordinarily appear to be quite strikingly reduced under the influence of the drug, although in some animal experiments small doses of the drug facilitated the learning processes. Characteristically, the electroencephalograms (brain-wave tests) show evidence of arousal, which appears to be due to a stimulatory affect on the midbrain.

Despite the range of unusual effects caused by this drug, it is not at all clear as to precisely how LSD acts. Its potency, however, is truly amazing. One kilogram is equivalent to slightly more than two pounds. One one-thousandth of a kilogram is a gram. One one-thousandth of a gram is a milligram. One one-thousandth of a milligram is a microgram, and only 100 to 250 micrograms need be administered by mouth to produce a potent four- to twelve-hour hallucinogenic experience. The power of the drug becomes even more apparent on analysis of blood levels of LSD. The tiny microgram unit can be broken down even further to nanograms, each nonogram being one one-thousandth of a microgram. After taking a conventional dose of LSD, only one to ten nanograms can be found in each cubic centimeter of blood, and very little of what is in the blood actually gets to the brain. One would think that a drug which is active after only a tiny amount is ingested must be concentrated in brain cells to produce such striking effects. Not true at all. In fact, most of the LSD taken is excreted through the liver into the intestinal tract, and the intestines, liver, kidney, adrenal gland, lungs, spleen, heart, muscles and skin all contain more of the drug than the brain. Nevertheless, LSD exerts profound behavioral effects; equally interesting, the influence on the nervous system may persist. Thus, in cats, a single administration of the drug produces changes in the electroencephalogram which can be detected as long as four to six days later. Similarly, in man, after a single ingestion of LSD the hallucinatory experience can return almost in its entirety weeks, months, even years later. In terms of behavioral characteristics in both man and experimental animals, mescaline, psilocybin and LSD, three of the most potent hallucinogens, appear quite similar.

In addition to the biochemical, pharmacological and physiological experiments, a substantial number of clinical studies have been performed during the last fifteen years which suggest that there are in fact a number of situations in which LSD might be beneficial or at least should be studied further. For instance, LSD taken on one to three occasions in dosages of 200 to 600 micrograms has been reported to effect sobriety or a profound reduction in alcohol intake in 20 to 60 per cent of severe chronic alcoholics. Two points deserve emphasis. First, in general, these studies have not been adequately controlled and frequently other therapeutic techniques were utilized simultaneously, thus clouding the specific role of the LSD. Second, a longer period of follow-up observation is needed, since recent studies suggest a striking drop-off in sobriety between the third and sixth month after the LSD experience. Third, three well controlled studies published in 1969 showed no advantages for LSD over other treatment modalities. Although its use is neither proved nor disproved in alcoholism, it does seem clear that some carefully selected patients, given the drug under strictly controlled circumstances, may demonstrate marked improvement in the excessive drinking pattern.

In cases of psychoneurosis, again one cannot say with assurance that LSD is clearly effective, but careful studies by several psychiatrists suggest that LSD may be strikingly beneficial in carefully screened patients. In a well-controlled therapeutic session use of the drug can bring to the surface an enormous amount of repressed material and permit far more ready transference between psychiatrist and patient. As a matter of fact, so much material may be elicited in a single LSD session that it may take months or even years to work through all the material with conventional psychiatric techniques. Those who appear to respond best are patients whose neurosis is characterized by phobias or compulsions. Here again it is not clear whether LSD is really more effective than conventional psychiatric therapy, but the collected data appear encouraging and continued investigation is surely warranted.

The data in respect to the treatment of psychopaths is still less conclusive. A psychopath is one who cannot tell the difference between right and wrong. This disease is notoriously refractory to any form of drug or psychiatric therapy. A report in England in the mid-1950s—as well as a more recent one in the United States—indicates that LSD may be beneficial in this condition, but informed opinion holds that these studies are not satisfactorily controlled, that the data are meager and that at present there is really little reason to believe that LSD will be any more successful in the treatment of psychopaths than any other form of therapy has been in the past.

A small number of cases of frigidity and sexual aberration have been treated with LSD, purportedly with good results. The best and perhaps the most enlightening study in this regard is that by J. R. Ball and Jean J. Armstrong, reported in the *Canadian Psychiatric Association Journal* in 1961. They treated ten patients with sexual aberrations who came to them seeking a cure for their deviancy. Two of the ten improved markedly, by objective standards. Most of the other eight stated that their behavioral paterns had changed strikingly for the better, but the therapists could detect no changes at all. Here then is an instance in which performance could readily be checked against alleged benefits—and in most of the cases the reported beneficial effects were found to be illusions.

Ordinarily LSD is considered contraindicted in true psychosis, such as schizophrenia. There are a few reports suggesting that the drug may be beneficial in schizophrenic children. Schizophrenia in childhood is an extraordinarily difficult disease to treat; for the most part, all therapeutic measures are doomed to failure. Consequently, any new technique which offers even the remotest hope of benefit is worthy of exploration. At this point LSD fits into that category. Small numbers of children have been studied, and some beneficial results have been reported, but the data are too limited to make even a preliminary conclusion. All one can say is that LSD treatment merits further investigation.

Together with alcoholism and psychoneurosis, cases of terminal disease represent perhaps the most intriguing area for potential use of LSD. Investigation of such use is in its nascent stages under the direction of Doctors Albert Kurland and Walter Pahnke in Maryland. Patients with lethal diseases accompanied by severe pain, requiring use of large amounts of opiates, have been given LSD on one to several occasions and in about half the cases either the amount of narcotic required has been profoundly reduced or the attitude of the patient has changed strikingly so that he or she is able to accept the inevitability of imminent death with a great deal more equanimity. In some of the cases both of these desired results were found. Despite public statements that LSD should be made available for the dying, it is crucial to emphasize that only a small number of patients have been treated. Here again the data are too few to permit even tentative conclusions although this, too, is an area in which a great deal more research is warranted.

In summary, there is at present no clearly documented place for LSD in medicine or psychiatry, but in three specific areas—alcoholism, psychoneurosis and terminal disease—the preliminary data are promising and a great deal more careful investigation should be encouraged.

During the ascendant period of LSD use, other well-publicized studies were performed, some on LSD per se and others on psilocybin, a less potent substance with similar effects. Dr. Keith S. Ditman and colleagues surveyed 74 patients and found that 72 per cent reported the LSD experience was pleasant. Leary, George Litwin and Ralph Metzner gave psilocybin to 175 subjects, 98 of whom filled out a questionnaire. In any study in which 175 subjects are given a drug and only 98, a little over half, fill out a questionnaire, the results are virtually impossible to interpret. However, among those responding, Leary and colleagues reported that 70 per cent had a very pleasant, wonderful or ecstatic experience, 88 per cent reported that they learned something of value or acquired tremendous insights. 62 per cent reported that the experience had changed them and their lives for the better. Dr. Leary and his colleagues performed an additional study with psilocybin, reported in 1965, suggesting that the administration of the drug reduced the recidivism rate in jailed adult offenders. These studies, too, have been criticized harshly as being totally uncontrolled, loosely structured and that in addition, despite the fact that the number returning to jail for new crimes was reduced, there was an increase among the psilocybin subjects in violation of parole. Here again, interpretation remains very difficult. Dr. Walter Pahnke performed a study in experimental mysticism using twenty graduate students with Protestant backgrounds from one denominational seminary. The experiment was performed on Good Friday, 1962; half the individuals were given psilocybin an hour and a half before the service began and all twenty then participated in a two-and-a-half-hour religious service. Afterward Pahnke made a careful study by questionnaire, which suggested to him that those who received psilocybin tended to have a genuine mystical experience. It is important to emphasize that these were divinity students and that although attempts were made at controls, such controls are impossible to maintain with potent hallucinogens in a subjective area such as mystical experiences since the subjects would very quickly know whether or not they had received the psilocybin or the placebo capsule. This was an important experiment but its interpretation must be limited to students having formal training in religion, taking the drug during a traditional religious service; the only real conclusion one can make is that additional studies of both divinity students and those with no religious training or background would be intriguing.

Initially it was hoped that the model psychosis produced by LSD would help investigators understand naturally occurring mental aberration. After substantial experimentation, it was concluded that the two were divergent. Thus, for example, the predominantly visual hallucinations induced by LSD are very different from schizophrenia in which the hallucinations are almost uniformly auditory. Then, too, schizophrenics frequently have true hallucinations whereas much of what we refer to as LSD-induced hallucinations are in reality illusions. During this period, Dr. Sidney Cohen assiduously collected data on an enormous number of cases of LSD administration under medical aegis, and reported that among normal individuals untoward reactions occurred in only .08 per cent while 1 in 830 of those in psychotherapy attempted suicide after LSD and 1 in 2,500 succeeded.

During the ascendancy of LSD then, the data from responsible investigators suggested that by and large the experience was pleasant and that the adverse reaction rate was relatively small. It is important to stress that at this time even the sociologic and attitudinal studies on LSD were being carried out in at least semi-controlled conditions. Extensive indiscriminate use did not really start until 1963 and did not become a wide-spread problem until 1965. It was between 1963 and 1965 that anecdotal reports on the pleasures of LSD were for the most part enthusiastic and unencumbered by warnings of potential dangers. While it seems unnecessary to go into these in any detail, I will cite a few from the published literature which exemplify the positive response to the LSD experience.

"Almost immediately several relationships that had escaped my attention became apparent and a solution followed soon after. I would guess that twenty minutes had elapsed. Normally, I would stew and fret for weeks before coming to such a solution."

"My experience during the session was an unbelievable increase in ability to concentrate and to make decisions. Anything was possible, three designs were outlined in three hours."

"Within the space of a few minutes I noticed that my hearing was extremely acute. The music sounded clearer than any I had ever heard before. In time the music became overwhelmingly beautiful, and I seemed to feel a satisfying swelling within my chest. I was now very conscious of the fact that the music was creating variations of great beauty in my own mind. It was such beauty that words cannot describe it. The word 'magnificent' kept running through my mind. I felt that I was being overwhelmed by beauty. I stated that I was undergoing the most magnificent experience of my life." (The unpredictability of the LSD experience is also shown by this patient's subsequent hallucinations and illusions: "I became aware that my mood had changed and I suddenly saw myself at the bottom of a huge filthy pit. It seemed to be bottomless and crawling with horrible things such as octopuses and enormous, odd-shaped frogs. I tried to crawl my way out of the pit and finally got near the top. Looking down it was horrible, worse than I have ever visualized hell. Sometime later, the doctor handed me a mirror—I looked but I didn't like what I saw. I watched to my utter horror as my image in the mirror began to age. My face became older and worn and I saw my skull disintegrate and turn into ashes and the ashes were me. In shock and horror I turned away from the mirror.")

"I was alone in a timeless world with no boundaries.

There was no atmosphere—there was no color, no imagery, but there may have been light. Suddenly I recognized that I was a moment in time created by those before me and in turn the creator of others. This was my moment, and my major function had been completed. By being born I had given meaning to my parents' existence."

"I became poignantly aware that the core of life is low. At this moment I felt that I was reaching out to the world to all people but especially to those closest to me."

"I was delighted to see that my skin was dissolving in tiny particles and floating away. I felt as though my outer shell was disintegrating and the essence of me being liberated to join in the essence of everything else about me. All this time I was drifting about in a wondrously beautiful heaven of visual imagery and music."

During this time there was great emphasis on the positive and ecstatic aspects of the experience. Colors were described as fantastic—more beautiful than anything the individual had ever seen before. All senses were heightened and co-mingled so that individuals could taste sound and hear light. Eating food during an LSD session was described as an extraordinary experience in which the individual could feel every fiber of the food on his tongue. The environment blended with self so that the person felt as one with others, with inanimate objects, with the hereafter and with the Deity. Inanimate objects took on magnificent life and appeared to quiver, breathe and pulsate. Time, space and body images were all markedly distorted and the sense of individuality disappeared. Religious figures appeared in the hallucinations, yet the whole experience often had a tremendously erotic overtone. Even during this period of celebration of the joys of the psychedelics, there was acknowledgment of bad trips and more frequently of experiences that were both pleasurable and horrifying. It was well known that one might see dismembered and mutilated bodies, or oneself dissolving into ashes. Some saw horrible animals which seemed to be trying to devour them. To some, a lighted cigarette appeared to be a writhing serpent snorting fire and wriggling towards them. The experience is so much a function of the individual personality that for each person it is totally different and unpredictable.

During the period of ascendancy the following assertions were made: The drug was incredibly potent. It was relatively safe. The good experiences far outweighed the bad. You could learn from it, gain insights, increase creativity and strip off the mask that prevents real understanding of life. You could expect an ecstatic experience characterized by incredible colors, ineffable beauty, love, eroticism and mysticism. After taking LSD there was a very good chance that your life would miraculously change for the better either in terms of performance or in your personal relationships. LSD showed great promise in medicine. LSD offered us a real hope of understanding the workings of the human mind.

This, then, was the promise and hope of LSD and the other potent hallucinogens. Huxley said it all when in 1957, in a talk before the New York Academy of Sciences, he said, "Pharmacology has now entered upon a period of rapid growth and it seems quite certain that in the next few years scores of new methods for changing the quality of consciousness will be discovered. The pharmacologist will give us something that most human beings have never had before; they will give us loving kindness, peace and joy. If we want beauty they will transfigure the outside world for us and open the door to visions of unimaginable riches and significance. If our desire is for life everlasting they will give us the next best thing, eons of blissful experience miraculously telescoped into a single hour."

Propelled by incredibly ebullient reports, by public panegyrics and an overwhelming torrent of predominantly favorable publicity, the drug caught on and escaped from scientific and medical control. In 1964 Sidney Cohen in his book *The Beyond Within* said, "Some of the young in mind who obtain the black market material will casually take it under dubious conditions, and without the necessary controls. Sooner or later they will find themselves caught in the grip of pure horror. With LSD the 'kicks' can go both ways." But the young in mind, the communications media and the LSD promoters were not listening. From early 1965 through 1967 we found ourselves in a period in which the promiscuous and indiscriminate use of LSD was epidemic; but it was during this period that the fantasies, illusions and ecstatic promises of the LSD adherents came face to face with reality.

CHAPTER EIGHT

LSD: ABUSE AND DISILLUSION

The claims were entrancing and seductive. LSD was supposed to enable you to learn a language within a week,
understand Einstein's theory of relativity, solve complex
mathematical problems immediately, or conceive magnificent architectural designs for hospitals, bridges or
buildings. Such claims are easy to make and difficult to
dispute. Interestingly, in my multiple debates with Timothy Leary, the most vocal and charismatic proponent
of LSD, he hardly ever made any statements concerning
its capacities for inducing creativity and never challenged
my dogmatic statements that LSD-induced creativity was
a myth. A reasonably objective study has been carried out
by Drs. William McGlothlin, Sidney Cohen and Marcella
McGlothlin in California. They gave LSD to twenty-four
subjects whose reactions were evaluated through an enormous battery of psychologic tests given prior to ingestion
of the drug, then two weeks afterward, and again six
months later. In addition, at the end of the six months,
each filled out a questionnaire. Creativity was measured
by analyzing the results of seven separate tests, including
the Thematic Apperception and Draw-a-Person tests. After six months, 25 per cent felt that the drug experience
resulted in enhanced creativity in their work. The seven
tests designed to measure creativity, however, showed no
changes at all. One can argue that these tests did not truly
measure creativity, but it does seem fair to note that this
careful attempt to objectively test creativity does not sup-

port the notion that LSD enhances this aspect of an individual's personality. These findings were confirmed in a study by Drs. L. S. Zegans, J. C. Pollard and D. Brown appearing in the *Archives of General Psychiatry* in 1967.

As with creativity, the term aesthetic sensibility refers to a somewhat nebulous characteristic which to some extent defies accurate measurement. The findings on the McGlothlin questionnaire reflect the general experience with the LSD; 62 per cent queried after the six-month interval noted a greater appreciation of music, and 46 per cent reported an enhanced appreciation of art. The five tests used to measure aesthetic sensitivity failed to show any significant changes. Once again the claims appear to conflict with the available objective data. One of the most important positive aspects of the LSD experience is said to be acquisition of insight into one's own personality and the relationship of the individual to the world at large. It is certainly true that in a therapeutic situation, with the aid of a trained psychiatrist or psychologist, LSD may help an individual attain meaningful insights, but when taken under non-medical aegis, the insights are either delusions or are so superficial that they have no lasting or significant effects on the individuals. Thus, for example, a young man came to Bellevue Hospital having by his own admission ingested an estimated 3,000 micrograms of LSD, this being approximately ten times the average human dose. Thereafter he became grossly psychotic, but recovered sufficiently after forty-eight hours of hospitalization to respond to questions. He was clearly well educated and sophisticated about drugs and was asked why he had taken such an enormous dose. His answer was, "I wanted either to kill myself or learn something about myself." He was then asked whether he had indeed gathered the insights for which he took the drug and he answered, "Yes, I learned a great deal about myself. I learned that I am basically egotistical." He surely could have achieved the same degree of self-knowledge through a brief period of honest introspection, without drugs; furthermore, this most superficial of insights, even if new, in no way modified his behavioral pattern. Many who take LSD describe their insights in a somewhat different fashion, as typified by the following remarks: "After taking acid I suddenly realized that what was important in the world and beautiful were the flowers and the sun and the sky and the grass and I recognized that all the games we play every day, all that materialistic crap, is just a lot of bullshit. I knew I didn't want to play those games any more and I decided to drop out, live my life in contemplation and appreciation of the beauty around me." Perhaps some would call this an insight, but most would consider it a facile rationalization for LSD-induced withdrawal from society.

One of the major claims of the proponents of the LSD experience is that it increases one's capacity to give or accept love. This too, of course, is almost impossible to measure accurately, but it seems to me very important to recognize that giving or accepting love connotes an in-depth relationship between two people, which mandates continuing communication between them. In many ways such a relationship is inconsistent with the LSD experience. LSD, more than any other illicitly used drug, places the individual in a very personal cocoon, spun out of illusion and hallucination. The experience is totally individualistic and self-centered, and therefore is diametrically opposed to the concept of love. This is not to say that after taking LSD one cannot have improvement in inter-personal relationships which appeared to be abrasive and unhappy prior to the use of the drug, but such apparently beneficial results do not, in most people, reflect an augmented capacity to love but rather diminished aggression and increased passivity.

There were also those who believed that LSD was an aphrodisiac. Chief among their number was Timothy Leary, who had a number of things to say on the subject. "There is no question that LSD is the most powerful aphrodisiac ever discovered by man." "The three inevitable goals of the LSD session are to discover and make love with God, to discover and make love with yourself, and to discover and make love with a woman." "In a carefully prepared loving LSD session a woman will inevitably have several hundred orgasms." "The sexual impact is of course the open but private secret about LSD which none of us has talked about in the last few years. If you announce that the psychedelic experience is basically a sexual experience, you are asking to bring the whole middle-aged, middle-class monolith down on your head. I feel I am free at this moment [September, 1966] to say what we've never said before, that sexual ecstasy is the basic reason for the current LSD boom." Those statements are patently incorrect. Yet as much as anything else they have been used to promote LSD. As soon as these claims were made, however, Leary was denounced by a variety of LSD exponents who pointed out that the one thing LSD was not, was a physical aphrodisiac. Everybody agrees that LSD causes striking mental eroticism. The images one sees, the figures, the fantasies, even religious figures, may be viewed in the delusional experiences in overwhelmingly erotic fashion. On occasion bizarre behavioral patterns can result. For example, one young woman took LSD and was subsequently lying in the middle of a public street, her dress pulled up, her legs far apart, moaning over and over again, "Come on God, fuck me." But the mental eroticism ordinarily has no physical counterpart. During the experience the individual is too interested in his imagery and his fantasy life to wish to be involved in sexual experiences. As one young lady in California put it, "It's like having sex all by yourself." And similarly, as one comes down from the experience or during the immediate aftermath, the tendency is to focus on the trip itself and the user infrequently shows any particular drive to achieve physical sexual gratification. This is not to say that people do not have sexual intercourse under the influence of LSD. The drug has been given to girls, sometimes without their knowledge, to put them in a position of such confusion and passivity that they could then be subjected to any sort of sexual activity including group orgies. Additionally, some persons under the influence of LSD may have sexual experiences which they describe in glowing or ecstatic terms. It should be emphasized that just as many who deliberately try to have intercourse under the influence of LSD are totally unable to do so. Even for the small number having intercourse under LSD, the alleged wonders of the experience are often related not to enhanced emotional content or love, but rather to distortions of perception. Thus, although the actual time elapsed might be relatively short, the individual might have thought that the period of copulation lasted for many hours, or the man might have had the illusion that he was not making love to a woman as such, but rather to a gigantic breast. Similarly the woman might feel that the man was in reality a gigantic penis which had entered her in all its six-foot splendor. Some people undoubtedly get their kicks out of this kind of distortion of the sexual experience, but its rarity should be stressed and it must be perfectly clear that such distortion in no way makes the sexual experience more loving or validly emotionally charged.

In summary, LSD is not an aphrodisiac. It produces mental eroticism which usually has no physical counterpart; this in fact makes the drug an anti-aphrodisiac. The facts, however, have not stopped the psychedelic cult from proselytizing LSD on the grounds that it is an aphrodisiac; indeed this erroneous claim has markedly accentuated the LSD problem.

At the opposite end of the spectrum, the original notion that LSD could in some way circumvent traditional religious experiences and permit the user to have immediate and direct communication with great religious leaders, with Christ or with God has for the most part not withstood the test of time. It certainly is true that LSD experiences are often characterized by hallucinations and illusions which have religious overtones, but once the LSD experience is over, there is no evidence that the religious aspect of the experience has had any lasting beneficial effects on the user. By definition a transcendental experience must have profound and long-lasting influence and effect specific and positive changes in behavioral patterns. Since this has not occurred under the influence of LSD, it would seem fair to conclude that the religious aspects of the LSD trip may well be pleasurable—and to certain individuals, especially those with religious training, meaningful—but they are not, in the conventional understanding of the term, transcendental.

In the end, the issue is a simple one. If one accepts the premise that LSD may be beneficial in certain rigidly defined circumstances when given under medical control and that the claims of benefit when taken under non-medical aegis are at best tenuous and ill documented, then the problem can be resolved simply by an analysis of the pleasure-to-danger ratio. There is no denying that for many people LSD taken in the most indiscriminate of circumstances is an exciting, enthralling and pleasurable experience, but the price one might have to pay for heightened sensations, glorious hallucinations, and ephemeral pleasures may be appallingly great.

A noted neurologist, Dr. Roy Grinker, writing in the *Archives of General Psychiatry* in 1963, said: "The drugs are indeed dangerous even when used under the best precautions. There are increasing numbers of reports that temporary or even permanent harm may be induced in spite of apparently careful pre-therapeutic screening of latent psychosis and careful precautions during the artificial psychosis. Here again is the story of evil results from the ill-advised use of a potentially useful drug due to unjustified claims, indiscriminate and premature publicity and lack of proper professional controls." Gradually, more and more reports of adverse effects appeared. Then in the fall of 1965, Doctors W. A. Frosch, E. S. Robbins and M. Stern of the psychiatric division at Bellevue Hospital, writing in the prestigious *New England Journal of Medicine*, described in detail twelve patients experiencing undesirable reactions serious enough to require hospitalization. This report, however, received little notice in the lay press, and the LSD bandwagon continued on its merry way until March, 1966, when the New York County Medical Society released a position paper enunciating for the first time what has since become the generally accepted position of the medical profession. In this report are summarized our observations on fifty-two cases admitted to Bellevue Hospital over an eight-month period, documenting many of the dangers connected with the taking of LSD. In the subsequent years a virtual avalanche of reports have added immensely to the weight of evidence concerning those dangers. A number of them are discussed below.

Any individual, no matter how well integrated into society, and whether or not he or she has any past history of psychiatric difficulty, can, after a single ingestion of LSD, suffer an acute psychotic break—severe enough to require hospitalization. The presence of a so-called guide or the administration of Thorazine pills, an LSD antidote, will reduce the severity of the psychotic reaction in some patients, but will not obviate the necessity for hospitalization in many others. Once acquired, the psychosis may last for days, weeks, months or even years. The precise percentage of LSD experimenters who will experience psychoses requiring hospitalization is not known, but the large number of LSD-induced psychoses seen in New York City and on the West Coast indicates that this is a major risk for any individual taking the drug promiscuously.

Overwhelming panic is another frequent concomitant of the LSD experience. Horrifying hallucinations, illusions and apparitions, fears of impending death or mutilation, terrifying convictions of permanent insanity, pervasive feelings of dissolution of the body or mind can produce panic of such severity that it is almost indescribable. Usually this disappears within a period of forty-eight to seventy-two hours after hospitalization but may persist for two to five weeks, especially in children and in those given LSD without their prior knowledge.

Severe emotional reactions can lead to other dangers. A fifteen-year-old boy in Philadelphia takes LSD, tells his mother he is going to bed and then either jumps or falls to his death from his bedroom window. A co-ed in San Francisco, a high school boy in Toronto, a young man in London, each goes out a window and plunges to his or her death. Under the influence of LSD people have jumped in front of trains, walked in front of speeding cars on freeways and trudged into the Pacific Ocean until they drowned. Whether these are intentional or inadvertent suicides is difficult to ascertain. One man who jumped in front of a train and survived told us that he had heard voices commanding him to do so. Another young boy who jumped out of a window and was severely injured but survived said that after taking LSD he found himself naked in the arms of another boy his age. He had had no history of sexual deviancy and, apparently incorrectly, interpreted the situation as homosexual, panicked, and took the quickest way out—which happened to be through the nearest open window. A physician who took LSD told me that he almost jumped out of a window, not because he had any intention of killing himself but because he saw such beauty outside that he was tempted to immerse himself in it as quickly as possible. Others have stated that they were convinced they could fly or that they were immune from any sort of physical injury. Whatever the mechanism in the individual case, it is absolutely clear that wherever LSD use has become prevalent, suicides and fatal accidents have always followed.

Self-mutilation, whether fatal or not, is a related phenomenon. A young student in California took LSD, looked in the mirror, saw the face of Christ and said to himself, "If Christ suffered why shouldn't I?" He went into the bathroom, took out a razor and slashed his throat and both wrists. A young woman under the influence of the drug doused herself with gasoline and turned herself into a human torch. Fortunately, the number of such cases which are adequately documented is at present still small.

The proponents of LSD use have long maintained that the drug does not induce violent or aggressive behavior. But the first description I heard of violence under the influence of LSD was from Dr. Leary himself, who described giving the drug to a very large man and then having to ask three of his associates to help him restrain the man after he became violent under the influence of the drug. At Bellevue Hospital 12.6 per cent of 114 patients studied were brought to the hospital because of uncontrolled violence or aggression. In one unusual case four college students took LSD together in New York City while on vacation. One suddenly turned to another and bit his cheek. Because of the drug's ability to reduce pain sensation the victim felt no discomfort and did not stop the attacker until a two inch chunk had been taken out of his cheek. This subsequently required multiple plastic surgery operations.

There have been perhaps a dozen homicides attributed to LSD. The most notorious of these was the killing of Mrs. Florence Cooper, a fifty-seven-year-old schoolteacher who was stabbed one hundred and five times by her thirty-two-year-old son-in-law, a former medical student. The killer claimed that he had taken LSD, and had no knowledge of the crime; he was subsequently acquitted on the grounds of temporary insanity. Two of the 114 patients we studied at Bellevue Hospital had attempted homicide—one tried to kill his mistress and another attempted to murder the two-year-old son of a girl friend.

Those who use LSD repeatedly may undergo a complete change in their value systems, rejecting ambition, work or financial success, which they come to regard as materialistic game-playing. Instead they withdraw into a solipsistic existence centered around drug-taking, endless philosophic discussions, and contemplation. For them, hallucinogenic drugs such as LSD are no longer an adjunct to their lives but become the center of existence

itself. In renouncing society for the perpetual illusions of
the drug experience, they not infrequently eschew family
and friends, preferring to live a drug-oriented communal
existence with others who have dropped out. One could,
of course, argue interminably about potential benefits
from such withdrawal, but most dispassionate observers
would agree that for the most part it represents a negativistic, narcissistic approach to life which in the long run
is nonviable.

Approximately one-sixth of the patients referred to
Bellevue Hospital for LSD-induced psychoses do not re-
cover during the hospital stay but must be referred to
other hospitals for possible long-term care. Only half of
these have histories of prior overt psychiatric abnormalities, but the incidence of severe underlying personality disturbance is probably substantially higher. Indeed the
current thinking is that for a normal, well-integrated individual, LSD psychoses may last for weeks or even months
but only rarely will persist indefinitely. On the other hand,
if the individual has substantial personality aberrations or
a neurosis, or a compensated psychosis, LSD may precipitate an active psychosis requiring hospitalization which
may persist for many months or years or even possibly result in permanent psychosis. Because studies on the untoward effects of LSD are relatively recent, it will obviously
be years before an assessment can be made as to the possibility that LSD-induced psychoses in a predisposed individual might lead to permanent severe mental aberration.
Currently one of the most pressing problems with LSD is
that an increasing percentage of those experimenting with
the drug are doing so with the hope of ameliorating or cur-
ing personality disturbances, and these, of course, are the
very people in whom an adverse reaction might result in a
prolonged stay in a mental hospital.

The most intriguing phenomenon associated with LSD
is the recurrence of unpleasant aspects of the experience
weeks, months or even years after LSD ingestion, even
though no additional drug is taken in the interim. I know

of one individual, for example, who appeared to be entirely normal; he took LSD on a single occasion at the request of his fiancée shortly prior to their marriage. For twelve hours he had what he described as a beautiful experience, but this was followed by twelve hours of overwhelming panic. Two years after this single ingestion of LSD he requested psychiatric advice because intermittently he continued to have panic reactions which were virtually identical to those he experienced during the second half of his initial LSD trip. During that two-year period the panic reactions had gradually diminished in intensity and it seems likely that over an additional period of months, or perhaps even years, the recurrent panic reactions will disappear. Similar occurrences have been reported with hallucinatory experiences, the hallucinations recurring intermittently up to two years after the initial experience, especially in periods of stress. The biochemical mechanisms underlying the remarkable phenomenon of recurrence remain an enigma.

The drug can also produce persisting anxiety and depression which virtually precludes the individual from functioning normally in society.

The evidence concerning purely physical damage caused by LSD continues to grow. Several patients have now been reported who developed generalized convulsions after taking the drug. And in California, four young students between the ages of eighteen and twenty-four stared at the sun while under the influence of LSD. Ordinarily, this would produce substantial discomfort, compelling an individual to close or avert his eyes. But these students felt no pain, continued to stare and permanently injured part of the retina, resulting in partial blindness. Again in California, two young men took what was alleged to be LSD and were found dead shortly thereafter. Toxicological studies of their tissues after autopsy revealed no other lethal chemicals and, at present, primarily because there has been no other cause established for their deaths, they are considered to have been the victims of an acute LSD overdose. But the most interesting and important physical damage caused by LSD is of a more subtle nature.

In the spring of 1967, Dr. Maimon Cohen and his colleagues from Buffalo observed that addition of tiny amounts of LSD to human white blood cells produced chromosomal breaks in a surprisingly high percentage of cells. Additionally, they noted that one individual who had repeatedly ingested LSD had similar changes. Soon thereafter Doctors Samuel Irwin and Jose Egozcue from Portland, Oregon confirmed these observations, noting chromosomal breaks in six out of eight users. As of March, 1970 the situation is as follows: In eight of fourteen studies chromosomal breaks and/or chromosomal rearrangements have been found in the white blood cells in approximately 80 per cent of LSD users. In general the greater the dose or the more frequent the use, the more likely that chromosomal abnormalities will be found. In the eight studies documenting chromosomal aberrations, the changes appear to mimic those found with radiation. Consequently, it is anticipated that they may be permanent. Thus far, the longest any individual has been studied after discontinuing LSD has been thirty months, and the changes have persisted until that time. Seven studies suggest that if a woman uses LSD during pregnancy there is a considerable chance her offspring will show chromosomal aberrations. The longest the infants have been studied is two and one-half years after birth, and the pattern of chromosomal abnormalities persisted. It has not been ascertained whether LSD produces chromosomal abnormalities in human reproductive tissues such as testes or ovaries, but in two of three experimental studies in mice the same chromosomal changes found in the blood were also detected in reproductive tissues. It is also not known whether the chromosomal defects will be passed on to the children if a mother who uses LSD discontinues it and subsequently becomes pregnant. Similarly, it is not known whether a male LSD user can pass the chromosomal breaks to his children.

At the present time, the evidence of chromosomal derangement is accompanied by three instances of infant abnormalities which may be related to maternal use of LSD.

The intriguing studies of man are buttressed by three of five studies of animals. In one study, mice were given a single injection of LSD intra-abdominally on the seventh day of pregnancy. Four days later the embryos were removed. Only 10 per cent of the control mice showed abnormalities as contrasted to 57 per cent of those given LSD. Generally similar results were found in a separate study in hamsters. The dosages used here were equivalent, on the basis of weight, to those administered to man. In the third study, rats were given small amounts of LSD on a single occasion early in pregnancy, which resulted in a very high incidence of subsequent stillbirths. In two other studies no fetal abnormalities were detected in rats after various dosage schedules of LSD.

To fully assess the genetic effects of LSD will take perhaps two generations. Since the kinds of chromosomal abnormalities found in the users mimic those found after radiation, the users must be observed particularly for the development of leukemia. As far as the offspring are concerned they might be defective at birth, or might develop physical or mental abnormalities five, ten, twenty, thirty or even forty years later. Furthermore, the genetic abnormalities might skip a generation so that a user's offspring, although bearing the chromosomal abnormality, would show no defects, but in the next generation major physical or mental aberration might arise. Although it will take a great deal of additional genetic and epidemiologic study to analyze fully the true meaning of the chromosomal abnormalities thus far demonstrated, it is fair to say that the medical profession would be unwilling ever to prescribe a drug which had such potential for genetic harm as does LSD unless there were very good reasons for doing so. In the light of our present knowledge, any person who takes LSD under non-medical aegis must be ignorant of the potential consequences, foolhardy, or suffer from substantial personality disturbances.

The reaction of the LSD proponents to the reports from Bellevue and other hospitals were intriguing. At first they denied that these patients had ever taken LSD; but this position became untenable when the patients themselves insisted that they had. That ploy having failed, they then insisted that the therapy given to the patients at Bellevue Hospital was entirely incorrect and, further, that the patients would have been much better off had they been immediately taken from the care of the Bellevue physicians and given over to non-medical LSD guides. In reply it was pointed out that nobody had asked these people to come to Bellevue Hospital; they either appeared of their own accord, because of overwhelming terror or other manifestations, or they were brought by relatives, the police, or even by LSD guides in cases where the situation had gotten out of hand. In these mental gyrations calculated to rationalize the Bellevue experience, the third step was to issue the facile statement that proponents of LSD had talked to the patients after their discharge from Bellevue and had found that the majority of them regarded the LSD experience, including the stay at Bellevue Hospital, as something beautiful and extremely worthwhile. To those of us who have worked for years at Bellevue Hospital, an anachronistic, cockroach-ridden institution woefully short of personnel and equipment, anyone insisting that hospitalization in the decrepit, overcrowded psychiatric division was a beautiful experience seems likely to be suffering at the very least from major impairment of judgment or even from a continuing psychosis. The final step in the attempts to absolve LSD when untoward reactions occur has been the insistence that the reports are egregiously exaggerated. This is typified by the debate over a five-year-old Brooklyn girl which can be found in the United States National Student Association 1967 collection of background papers on student drug involvement. One of the papers records a debate between one of the gurus of the LSD movement, Allen Ginsberg, the poet, and James Fox of the Food and Drug Administration. The following are quotes from Ginsberg's presentation: "One of the most traumatic incidents which took place in the last year was the little girl in Brooklyn who ate a sugar cube of LSD in her icebox—you read all about that or heard about it. That actually was one of the things that really started the journalistic craze and tipped off like a whole mass hysteria. The *New York Post* on April 6, 1966, Wednesday, no byline, 'Girl Eats LSD and Goes Wild.' People who swallowed LSD went berserk. Some have killed, several deaths have been reported, sometimes because of the toxic effect of the drug and sometimes because of the hallucinations that lead to suicide. Well, that is absolutely bullshit. Twenty-four hours later: 'Five-year-old Donna Wingenroth fought for life today after swallowing LSD-coated sugar cube she found in the family refrigerator. The blonde little Brooklyn girl was reported still in 'very critical condition' eighteen hours after the doctors had pumped her stomach and treated her for convulsions in Kings County Hospital.' Well, it's a wonder she survived that, that hysteria on the part of the *New York Post,* the Kings County Hospital and the mass hysteria of the atmosphere of New York that day. For what actually happened, now the *New York Telegram and Sun,* April 14, 1966—here is like a reprieve. Here is what actually happened. 'LSD Girl Home—Condition Seems Normal. Donna was released from Kings County Hospital in apparently normal condition. Donna began to behave normally again within hours after arrival at Kings County Hospital, according to the assistant hospital administrator. Despite this, she was placed on the critical list and kept under close observation by pediatricians and neurologists to test her reflexes and all her functions before she was released.' They had not had a case like that so they put her on the critical list for that reason. It was just to keep close scientific track of her. Now it was on the basis of this case and another case built up in the newspaper that

Brooklyn District Attorney Koota called a conference of law enforcement officials and insisted that Travia, the head Senator from the New York State Legislature, rush a bill for New York State making sale or possession of LSD a crime. It was this same incident that was mentioned by Dr. Donald B. Louria, chairman of the New York County Medical Society, in letters to the *New York Times* and interviews with the press when he was also pushing for extreme and rapid legislation to control the immediate dangerous problem."

Ginsberg, on the one hand, accuses the newspapers of hysteria for reporting what he does not like and, on the other, accepts without reservation another newspaper report that appears to support his point of view. He did this without any perceptible personal investigation of what really happened to the girl, and used this line of reasoning to convince young people that LSD is not really dangerous and that what happened to this little girl was an example of exaggeration and hysteria. Well, what are the facts? In the *Journal of the American Medical Association* in the fall of 1967 there is an article titled: "An Untoward Reaction to Accidental Ingestion of LSD in a Five-Year-Old Girl." The girl, the one referred to by Mr. Ginsberg, was hospitalized in April, 1966. At that time, according to the article, "she was alternately screaming and silent. During her quiet periods she was motionless and unresponsive, and apparently unaware of her surroundings." Five hours later she was suffering from delusions, including one that her body was cut off at the waist. Her electroencephalogram (brain-wave test) was abnormal. On admission her intelligence quotient (IQ) was found to be 108 and thereafter fell to 94. Her drawings showed incoordination, disorganization and poor planning. She was discharged one week later, but at that time had continued distortion of the body image. It took five months for her IQ to return to its normal level of 125. Her electroencephalogram remained abnormal for the *entire five-month period*. At the end of nine months she was much improved, but at that time her visual motor functions, as tested by copying geometric figures, were still disorganized, uncoordinated and impaired. Now that is not an uncritical newspaper report and it surely is not consistent with Mr. Ginsberg's breezy dismissal of the whole incident as newspaper hysteria. Instead it is a carefully documented medical analysis of a young girl made horrendously sick by the inadvertent ingestion of an enormously dangerous drug.

The same facile approach is currently being used in regard to the chromosomal abnormalities. It is said aspirin, tranquilizers, antibiotics, caffeine and measles vaccine produce the same chromosomal defects and therefore the findings with LSD are meaningless. This just is not so. Aspirin-induced chromosomal breaks have been found only in the test tube, not in man. The breaks noted after administration of tranquilizers or live measles vaccine are transient and do not persist as do those observed with LSD. Antibiotics do indeed produce severe chromosomal abnormalities but these are anti-cancer antibiotics, not the ones used in everyday medicine to treat infections. The studies on caffeine have been carried out for the most part in the fruit fly. The calculated equivalent dose in man to produce chromosome derangement would be 30 gallons of coffee daily and so far no chromosomal defects have been found in inveterate coffee drinkers. Thus the attempts to dismiss the potential genetic dangers of LSD by comparison with commonly used drugs are unjustified. The actual frequency of chromosomal abnormality and the consequent genetic risk to the LSD user or the users' progeny can only be ascertained by careful and prolonged scientific analysis; the physical dangers due to chromosomal defects cannot be established by premature and emotional newspaper or magazine stories nor can they be disproved by merely derogating the data or utilizing invalid comparisons.

The LSD movement as an isolated phenomenon has reached a plateau and should over the next few years decline. There are six fundamental reasons for this. First, the movement was carried forward on the shoulders of a small number of charismatic leaders, some of whom have lost much of their ability to communicate with and influence young persons. Second, after the communications media had had their heyday promoting the LSD cult and exploring its putative pleasures, they found that the news value of drugs had shifted and they turned to detailed and often lurid descriptions of the harmful effects of the drug. No user can now avoid being exposed to the catalogue of potential dangers, and this avalanche of bad publicity further impedes the progress of the LSD movement.

A third reason for the waning of LSD use is that the cult has become inextricably entangled with multiple drug use as a result; there are now no pure LSD movements, for among the drug sub-culture LSD is merely one of a conglomeration of drugs taken simply for the love of being intoxicated. This indiscriminate usage effectively removes LSD from its pedestal; no longer can it be taken so seriously, either as the sacrament of a new religion or as a means of seeking valid insights or mind expansion. Dr. William Frosch and his colleagues reporting in the *Psychiatric Quarterly* in January, 1967, noted, "A surprisingly small percentage said they took the drug primarily for its beneficial effects. Only two patients [of thirty-four] took LSD to achieve personality improvement by way of psychedelic experience. Fourteen sought kicks or highs and the rest, although primarily interested in excitement or companionship, said they would not have minded if they were helped psychologically in addition to achieving an experience." The idealism of the initial proponents of LSD has been irrevocably eroded by the kicks orientation of the hippies.

Then, too, those taking LSD for specific purposes generally found that it was all shadow and no substance. If they sought sexual prowess they found instead only erotic hallucinations. If they sought transcendental experiences, they received only religious illusions. Those who hoped the drug would inspire creativity found that instead it reduced their ambition to be creative. The promise and the reality of LSD were disparate. In addition, the whole psychedelic movement has become invaded by commercialism; an enormous number of persons both within and external to the LSD movement quickly recognized the incredible amount of money that could be made out of it. Even the knowledge that by early 1967 Dr. Leary's fee had risen to a minimum of $1,000 per lecture was enough to dampen the ardor of some potential converts. The psychedelic discotheques, the psychedelic delicatessens, the plays, the motion pictures and organizations such as Sensefex, which "has analyzed the visual effects of psychedelic experience, has reduced it to an electric formula and has boxed it into a controlled system which can be operated by one person," vitiate the mystique of a supposedly aesthetic, pseudo-religious, anti-materialistic drug movement. After all, it is quite difficult to have a movement which on the one hand adopts as its shibboleth rejection of a materialistic, money-grabbing society, and simultaneously uses the movement itself for enormous financial gains.

Finally, as the dangers of LSD became known, society reacted with new laws. Until 1965 there were no laws which forbade or governed potent hallucinogens. But this has been remedied. Currently, at the federal level, one can go to jail for up to five years for illicit manufacture, sale or distribution of LSD, and for up to one year for illegal possession alone. Approximately one-half of the states by early 1968 had made both sale and possession of LSD a crime, with potential sentences ranging in the different states from up to one year to up to ten years in jail. Additionally, the Food and Drug Administration began a concerted effort to reduce the illicit supply.

As of this writing in 1968, the LSD movement is very alive, but the incidence of use appears to have leveled off, the image of the movement has been tarnished and the fears of potential genetic damage are causing many young persons to have second thoughts about experimenting with LSD and similar mind-altering drugs. Like many other fads which have transiently swept the country, the brief period of LSD ascendancy appears past and we are now entering a period of disillusion and acceptance of reality.

CHAPTER NINE

TURNING OTHERS ON

"I turned on two hundred fellow-students at the University of Michigan" (*Esquire*, September, 1967); "This friend of mine had been trying to turn me on for three months, so I let him" (*New York Post,* October 18, 1967); "The thing I would like to do most in life is turn on a football player" (student at a major Eastern college); "It has been observed that cannabis addicts always try to persuade their friends and acquaintances to try these drugs by attributing all sorts of wonderful properties to them" (Chopra, writing in the *U.N. Bulletin on Narcotics* of his experience with the use of cannabis drugs in India).

These statements, all relating to marihuana or other forms of cannabis are a typical representation of the most pernicious aspect of the drug movement—namely that a substantial proportion of those in the drug sub-culture become zealots and missionaries determined to turn everyone else on. This is true not only with marihuana but even more so with LSD. In the Haight-Ashbury district of San Francisco nine-year-old children have been given candy coated with LSD, resulting in their being hospitalized with acute panic reactions and acute psychoses. Hippie mothers blow marihuana smoke in the faces of their infant offspring, or give their children LSD to protect them from the hang-ups of the world. There are always rationalizations for this kind of behavior—they say they do it to give others pleasure, to free them from anxiety, to expand their minds, to instill love in them, to help rescue them from the horrors of the real world or merely because they want to see what the individual will be like when he is stoned. But whatever the rationalization, the psychedelic proselytizers who turn others on are not just doing their own thing, not just enjoying their own intoxication; they are foisting it on other people regardless of the potential deleterious consequences. This phenomenon is not limited to hallucinogenic drugs such as cannabis and LSD alone. It is also characteristic of users of other drugs, such as central stimulants and heroin. Amphetamine or Methedrine users urge these stimulants on others, and for a heroin user it is considered the greatest of achievements to "give somebody their wings," which means either injecting someone with heroin intravenously or teaching the person how to inject himself.

The crucial question is, of course, why? One can argue that LSD has such profound effects on the individual that users become utterly convinced of the drug's capacity to induce beauty, and so develop an evangelical spirit out of the simple desire to share these wonders with others. But the high from marihuana is limited; it makes many people feel good, but surely it is not potent enough to cause individuals to devote their lives to trying to turn other people on. And as the missionary spirit is found not only in connection with hallucinogenic drugs but also with stimulants, opiates and depressants, it would seem that there is something more fundamental linking drug abuse and the tendency among some users to become proselytizing zealots. Perhaps the following hypothesis will answer some of these questions.

Once an individual becomes involved in, and committed to, drug abuse, whether the drug is an amphetamine-like stimulant, heroin, marihuana or LSD, he is by the very nature of his illicit drug use to some extent a pariah. The feeling of being an outcast is far greater in those driven to their drug abuse by underlying personality defects often characterized by alienation, despair, repressed aggressions or immaturity. These people, especially the heavy users—

potheads, acid-heads, amphetamine habitués, heroin addicts—are convinced, in part because of their drug use,
that they can no longer participate in the so-called straight
society. Adamant in the belief that they cannot join society, they try to bring society to them by turning others on,
seemingly with the vague hope that if everybody is turned
on, then they will no longer feel like outsiders. In some
instances, of course, this is too complex an explanation,
especially in the case of marihuana in which attempts to
turn others on may represent nothing more than youthful
enthusiasm. Whatever the reason, the avid attempts of the
drug sub-culture to gain new converts by active proselytizing is an intrinsic aspect of the movement and cannot be
disregarded.

In 1967 a small informal survey was conducted among
students at a major Eastern college. Six per cent said they
had used LSD, but an additional one-third indicated that
they either would or might take the drug without medical
supervision. From this and other studies, it would seem
that young people can be divided into three groups. The
first group is already committed to the drug experience,
but these individuals make up no more than 5 to 10 per
cent of the youthful population; the second group, at the
other end of the spectrum, could not be induced under
almost any circumstances to indulge in illicit drug-taking.
The third group, often the majority of any given college
population, is not likely to seek out the drug experience
deliberately, but at the same time will not recoil from it.
Curious and educable, they can be readily subverted to
drug abuse by the seductive blandishments of those users
dedicated to turning everyone else on. The phenomenon
of turning on others presents high school and college
administrators, as well as society as a whole, with a real
quandary. If a benign attitude is adopted toward illicit
users of drugs such as marihuana and LSD, many users
will simply continue their involvement with drugs and go
their own ways, but others will insist on devoting their
energies to increasing the size of their drug sub-culture.

Given an insouciant attitude on the part of a school administration, a proselytizing minority of 5 per cent could subvert the majority in short order. This in essence is what happened in England over the last five years regarding heroin use, and the result has been an increase of over 2,000 per cent in youthful heroin users in that country. It is happening in this country now with marihuana. The only sensible approach, it would seem, is for high schools and colleges to establish specific rules and regulations in regard to drug use and then to react vigorously when students are caught violating those regulations; for if the peer-group proselytizers are not forced to desist, or removed from the environment, the situation will ineluctably get worse.

No group has been more dedicated to turning everyone else on than the hippies. The hippie movement was invested with an enormous amount of attractiveness and nobility by a wide variety of educators, sociologists, psychologists and religious leaders. According to the positive view, it is characterized by lofty ideals and by the rejection of an achievement-oriented, materialistic society which the hippies believe is traveling a one-way road to disaster. The hippie finds the Western world dehumanized and power-crazy, cruel and avaricious. The hippies reject war and extol love, spontaneity, joy, harmony, truth, beauty and the wonders of nature. Propelled by a tidal wave of enthusiastic publicity starting in the fall of 1966, the movement grew enormously until mid-1967. In 1968, the communications media decided it wasn't quite as glorious as it once was. Having built it up, they now found it made equally good copy to tear it down, and as a result the growth of the hippie movement leveled off and is now actively receding. I shall attempt no detailed judgment of the putative glories of the philosophic platitudes that dominate the movement, but it does seem to me that a number of points are important about the hippie movement as it relates to drug abuse. Despite the large number of conflicting philosophies said to be central to the hippie movement, one vital fact emerges: it has been and still is virtually impossible to be committed to the hippie movement without using at least marihuana and usually a farrago of other drugs including LSD and amphetamines. It is basically a drug movement and anything which holds the promise of intoxication will be extensively utilized. In 1966 and early 1967 the hippie drugs of choice were marihuana and LSD, but by mid-1967 at least as much oral amphetamine or intravenous Methedrine was being used—drugs which act as energizers and stimulants, have tremendous toxicity, and are diametrically opposed to marihuana and LSD in the behavioral patterns they induce. Walk down the main street of any hippie center and offer the contents of an unlabeled bag of pills or capsules as you go—you will find a myriad of takers who are uninterested in the content of the pills so long as there is a potential for getting high.

Another intriguing aspect of drug use in the hippie sub-culture, and clearly indicative of their commitment to drugs, is the intermittent use of heroin. Approximately half the hippie-type LSD users now coming to Bellevue Hospital for psychiatric help have experimented with heroin. These findings have been confirmed by other investigators. Only infrequently does the hippie heroin user actually become addicted, but because the drug offers the promise of intoxication they do experiment with it, just as they will experiment with any other drug available. One cannot glorify hippies or the hippie movement without simultaneously condoning the use of any and every intoxicating drug which may give people kicks. Those who support the movement or invest it with philosophical nobility tend to ignore or minimize the overwhelming evidence indicating that without drugs there is no hippie movement.

Initially the hippies were an outgrowth of the beatniks and were dominated by artists, poets and those I have called seekers. For the most part, these people, many of whom had a great deal of importance to say to and about

our society, have left the movement or remain in name
only. A large percentage of those currently committed to
the hippie existence are not in fact valid seekers for truth
and beauty; rather, they are using facile statements of
noble purpose as a cover for their own personal depression, alienation and consequent use of the drugs which
permit them to withdraw from society. For them the
hippie life is not so much a positive expression as a
manifestation of rejection and pervasive unhappiness.

Hippies talk of love incessantly, but, dominated as it is
by drug use, the movement is basically narcissistic and
inwardly focused; its members are for the most part incapable of either accepting or giving love in the conventional sense of the word. However, since love is felt to be
synonymous with sex, extraordinary promiscuity characterizes the hippie behavior pattern, and the medical problems engendered by the movement have been enormous.
The hippie girls tend to be passive and willing to participate in virtually any type of sexual activity. There is much
group sexual activity as well as a substantial amount of
male and female homosexuality. One consequence of this
extensive heterosexual, bisexual and homosexual activity
has been an alarming rise in the venereal disease rate.
Additionally, the intravenous use of Methedrine and heroin and the administration of drugs by communal unsterilized needles have resulted in an astounding incidence of
hepatitis.

Joining the hippies are the young teeny-boppers as well
as a whole variety of individuals merely out for sex or
kicks. For example, in the San Francisco area, the Haight-
Ashbury district is adjacent to the Filmore district, a
Negro slum, in which heroin use is rampant. Because of
the availability of the hippie girls, the young men from the
Filmore district moved into the Haight-Ashbury area. Although they did not become committed hippies, they did
participate both in the sex and the drug behavior patterns.
In addition they brought along their own drug contribution, heroin, introducing it into a movement which up

until that time had been dominated by marihuana and LSD. Similarly, motorcycle-riding, amphetamine-taking young hoodlums joined the movement in San Francisco solely because that's where the action seemed to be and where the girls were. They, too, brought their drug contribution, the central stimulants, which rapidly became an integral part of the hippie sub-culture. Once the misfits, thrill seekers and delinquent sociopaths joined the hippie movement, it became increasingly tawdry and sordid.

The death knell of what may have started as a valid movement has been sounded by the surprising union of the hippie movement with outlaw motorcycle gangs. In the Haight-Ashbury district of San Francisco, police are detested, and the protectors for the hippies are Hell's Angels and other motorcycle thugs. Thus the hippies who talk so glibly of love, gentleness and kindness have joined forces with one of the worst groups of hoodlums in this country. The following three examples will serve to illustrate the influence of the motorcycle gangs.

In July, 1967 a young man sold what was allegedly LSD to some hippies, but instead they got "burned," meaning that they paid for material that was not LSD. They reported this to their protectors, who then arranged to have the young man invited to a party to which a number of the motorcyclists were also invited. At what they considered an appropriate time, the young man was dragged outside and beaten up so thoroughly that five weeks later he remained hospitalized with what appeared to be permanent brain damage.

In the same month in the spring of 1967, the physician-director of a medical clinic supplying free care to hippies found that some $28 had been stolen from the medical clinic. This was reported to the "protectors" and eventually the culprit was found. The doctor then had to spend an entire night with the "protectors" explaining that if they meted out the punishment they intended, specifically a vicious beating, the clinic would have to close as such actions would be incompatible with the purpose of the clinic. When I was visiting the clinic, a fight and a minor stabbing occurred just outside. A hippie who had witnessed the fray rushed into the clinic to describe it. The following conversation took place.

"What happened down there?"

"These two guys got into a fight and one cut the other a little but it wasn't too bad."

"What happened to the guy who did it?"

"Oh, he took off and I saw a couple of the Angels take off after him."

"Well, I hope for his sake they didn't catch him."

A similar situation has developed in Buffalo where a legalize-marihuana group has formed something called the Trans-love Commune. This group despises the local law enforcement agencies, as illustrated by this promulgation: "Warning, under no circumstances should you cooperate with your local police and narcotics squad. They are corrupt, armed and dangerous." Despising the law, the hippie group turned to an outlaw motorcycle gang called the Road Vultures for protection, as in San Francisco. The following example taken from the literature published by the hippie group is indicative of the extent to which the hippies distrust the law and rely on local hoodlums.

"Trans-loves next contact with the Road Vultures came at a very bad moment in our lives. Four motorcyclists rode by the Hot Area one night and I thought they were RV's come to say hello. We had been meaning to get together and talk to each other for some time since the be-in. It turns out that these four riders were not Vultures though one, the youngest, claimed to have ridden with the RV's in the past. One girl from the Trans-love Commune accepted a ride with these guys thinking no doubt of friendship between hippies and motorcycle gangs in the West. The girl came back several hours later having endured a vicious ordeal of repeated rape for those hours, in three different houses several times by three of the four guys. The word is gang bang. She was not beat up physically but she sure was spaced out mentally for three or four days afterward. We were at a loss about what to do. The riders had said they would be back that very night. Calling the cops was out of the question so we thought of the Road Vultures for help. Three of us went out that very afternoon and met Tom Bell (the leader of the Road Vultures who was subsequently killed in a brawl) and some of the men. I will say no more in print (because it might be picked up by the fuzz and be incriminating), but the RV's helped us cool these other riders so they are no longer a threat to us. It is strange when in Buffalo hippies must rely on an 'outlaw' motorcycle gang, rather than the cops, to get justice done."

This episode surely indicates at the very least, confusion and a lack of judgment. Whatever the rationalization of the hippie community may be, there is no way in which an allegedly gentle love-movement can adequately justify or explain joining forces with organized viciousness. When the hippies call on the thugs and the latter administer justice in their cruel perverted fashion, the hippies are guilty by association. It makes a mockery of their façade of love and kindness.

Another form of violence invading the hippie movement is exemplified by the grisly murders of Linda Fitzpatrick and James Hutchinson in New York City's East Village. The girl, from a wealthy Greenwich, Connecticut family, had left home and lived with a variety of people in Greenwich Village. Her boyfriend, Hutchinson, well known in the East Village by the name of Groovy, was noted in part for using, selling and giving away a whole variety of drugs. Both the victims had used not only marihuana and LSD but also Methedrine, the central stimulant popularly called speed. Lured to a filthy basement apartment in the East Village, the two participated in a drug party, following which Linda was repeatedly raped; she and Hutchinson were then beaten to death. Arrested almost immediately and charged with murder were two young Negroes, Donald Ramsey, a twenty-six-year-old ex-convict and Thomas Dennis, twenty-six, also a resident of the East Village. Although it was widely believed that the drug being used at the party which ended in the murders was LSD, there is now an increasing conviction that the drug was Methedrine. This would be far more consistent with our knowledge of Methedrine action. This drug, increasingly popular among the hippies, reduces inhibitions, augments sensory awareness, increases energy enormously and is also, at least for some people, an aphrodisiac; in addition, it characteristically produces paranoia.

In Sweden, where similar stimulants are used, paranoia and excess energy result from drug abuse but in that country, little noted for its violence, marked aggression is ordinarily not found as a consequence of stimulant use. In the United States it is likely to be far different. Here violence has been an intrinsic part of our society since the birth of the nation. Give Methedrine or similar stimulants intravenously to a basically aggressive person, and the combination of diminished inhibitions, increased energy, augmented sexual interest and paranoia will ineluctably lead in some people to rape, beatings and murder. Although they are the most publicized, Linda Fitzpatrick and James Hutchinson's deaths are by no means the first in the hippie community—nor will they be the last.

The police in San Francisco are now noting a striking increase in beatings and homicides in the Haight-Ashbury district, and the number of violent crimes will increase progressively as long as stimulants such as Methedrine are utilized by a hippie sub-culture which is increasingly inundated, both at its core and on the fringes, by basically angry and aggressive sociopaths. Indeed, in the first six months of 1969 in the Haight-Ashbury district over thirty murders correlated with heavy use of Methedrine. The hippie movement appears in the end to be nonviable. It is a cop-out on the world of reality; the hippies are committed not to solving problems but to withdrawing from them. It is a pleasure-oriented movement which has become tawdry, sordid and aggressive. Whatever its original purpose, it now has little to say or contribute. The original hippies either have moved on to other movements such as rural communes or are submerged beneath the hedonistic newcomers. Those who continue to extol the current hippie movement disregard its overwhelmingly negative aspects and unwittingly encourage drug abuse.

CHAPTER TEN

THE TREATMENT OF OPIATE ADDICTION

So much has been written in recent years about effective new treatment programs for heroin addicts that it seems pertinent to summarize the current status of the most important ones. But before detailing specific programs it is important to emphasize three points. First, narcotic addiction is not an incurable disease. It is well recognized that the number of known addicts drops strikingly after age thirty. This reduction in the addict population in the fourth and fifth decades of life cannot be accounted for by death, incarceration or the ability to escape detection. Rather it has been suggested that addicts "grow out" of their addiction, presumably when they become committed to other activities in life and no longer need the heroin as a crutch. What percentage do indeed mature out of their heroin habit is not known, but it seems clear that the number is large. Indeed a study by Drs. Lee N. Robins and George E. Murphy published in the *American Journal of Public Health* in 1967 suggested that as many as 80 per cent may "grow out" of their heroin addiction by their mid-30s. Others feel the percentage of "growing out" is much smaller.

Secondly, the widely quoted figures on relapse rates give an erroneous picture of the long-term recovery rate. The figures from the narcotic rehabilitation unit at Lexington, Kentucky, for example, show that 95 per cent of people leaving that institution use heroin again within a period of six months. However, if those same people are followed for a period of time—five years—the voluntary abstinence rate eventually rises to 25 per cent. And if they are followed for ten years, it increases further to 42 per cent.

Third, several studies demonstrate clearly the importance of supervision once the individual returns to the community. The New York State Division of Parole and the New York City Parole Commission followed over 1,200 addicts for a prolonged period of time. Despite the fact that these were drawn from an unmotivated, jailed population, the long-term satisfactory adjustment rate, defined as gainful employment and no return to drugs, was approximately 30 per cent. In sharp contrast, there was virtually no supervision of young addicts discharged from the Riverside Hospital in New York City, and there the relapse rate was almost 100 per cent. These results have been confirmed by data from the Lexington facility by Dr. George Vaillant which showed that those under probation or parole are much more likely to remain drug-free than those who have no such external controls.

Fourth, the addict who spends most of his time stealing to obtain money for his heroin habit, is often psychologically but not physically addicted. (The addict will burglarize, pilfer, forge prescriptions or prostitute but there is no evidence addicts are prone to commit crimes of violence.) At Bellevue Hospital we now try to withdraw heroin users with $20-40 a day habits (4-8 injections) *without* substitute drugs and only rarely do they develop significant withdrawal symptoms. A few years ago this would have been impossible. The addict of today is not truly physically addicted because the venal purveyors are adulterating the heroin extensively with quinine or milk sugar. It is thus usually easy to withdraw addicts from their heroin; indeed it is assumed the addict takes at least 150 milligrams a day of heroin but, in point of fact, it is likely his total daily dose is nearer half that amount.

In 1964, at the Rockefeller University Hospital in New York City, an experiment was initiated in which heroin addicts were given oral methadone as a substitute for heroin in the hope that it would block their narcotic need and permit them to be rehabilitated. The program consists of six weeks of inpatient status, during which the individual is taken off heroin and given as maintenance a large dose, approximately 80 to 120 milligrams, of methadone, a synthetic narcotic which keeps the individual addicted, but prevents him from getting any kick from injecting additional amounts of heroin. The hypothesis is that if an addict can no longer get a kick from his heroin, he will abandon the criminal activities which made it possible for him to obtain the drug and will then be susceptible to rehabilitation. Encouraged by early results, the program has been markedly expanded under the aegis of Dr. Vincent Dole, an internist, and Dr. Marie Nyswander, a psychiatrist. Recently a spate of enthusiastic reports have appeared suggesting that this may well be a panacea for drug addiction. As of January 1, 1970, a total of over 2,000 patients had been admitted to the program, and of those admitted about 80 per cent remained in the program. Approximately one third of those in the program six months or longer either continued on welfare or were employed by the program. A second one third either were students or were employed intermittently, and the final one third could be considered steadily employed. These results are very encouraging indeed, but there are several caveats which must be carefully considered.

First, the program is open only to volunteers, and of those who volunteer, many are rejected. Thus one must be well motivated to begin with, and even such motivation does not guarantee acceptance into the program. Since no more than 40 per cent of addicts, and perhaps as few as 20 per cent, are indeed well motivated and since the program accepts only half of the motivated people who apply, it is clear that in its present form it could reach only 20 per cent of the addict population at most. In addition, the average age of those in the program is thirty-two years, which is within the early phases of the maturing-out period; therefore, it is important to ascertain whether these people are doing well simply because they are in the older age category. It is implied that virtually all people admitted to the program become constructive members of society or desist from antisocial activities. This is not so. 18 per cent of those receiving methadone have been arrested; indeed, several have been discharged from the program for selling their methadone. However, as the arrest rate for a control-addict population during the same period is 45 per cent, it is clear that even though antisocial activity is not entirely curtailed by the methadone program, it is substantially reduced.

There is evidence that some of the individuals on methadone maintenance turn to other drugs including marihuana, amphetamines, barbiturates and alcohol. As a matter of fact, one of the patients died of barbiturate overdose and another of acute alcoholism. If an individual merely substitutes the heavy abuse of other drugs for his heroin addiction, then clearly the rehabilitation program has not been successful. The impression given by some of the proponents of the program is that methadone itself produces the rehabilitation. What they do not stress, but should, is that numerous supplemental rehabilitative techniques are used. For instance, these people are given special consideration at welfare centers and special opportunities for job retraining. To imply that merely giving methadone has rehabilitated anyone is clearly misleading. Then, too, several other methadone-maintenance programs have been initiated which have not been nearly so successful. In one, only three out of fifteen addicts could be said to be doing well under methadone. Another failed before it ever got started because well-motivated addicts could not be recruited for the program. In a third program in Canada, of 321 addicts who started with methadone, 264 dropped out of the program; of the 57 who remained on the drug, most did well, but those in charge of the program feel that if a high percentage of successes is to be achieved, then greater and greater rigidity in selection of addicts must be employed. They stress that there must be clear expectation of a job and evidence of stability in other aspects of the addict's life. Thus methadone is no panacea. Like all the other programs discussed here, it is in its experimental stages, and suggestions that it is now ready for general applicability are just not valid. It is not nearly as good as its proponents would have us believe, although for a small number of carefully selected individuals it is clearly beneficial. Only time will tell what percentage of the addict population will actually benefit from this kind of therapy.

Synanon is a non-medically oriented group-living program begun in 1958; since that time it has served some 2,000 addicts. Unfortunately, Synanon has not undergone careful extramural scrutiny. Its program consists of removing the addict from his environment and bringing him into a group-living residential program run by ex-drug users. No drugs are administered. Initially the addict is treated like a child but if all goes well he gradually assumes more and more responsibility within the Synanon community. The crux of the treatment program is the group symposium, in which the participants talk about a variety of topics but especially about themselves and their colleagues, often in brutal fashion, the hypothesis being that the façade of the drug addict must be sundered and the individual forced to accept himself as he is. After such acceptance of self, he can then attempt to reconstruct his personality preparatory to assuming a constructive place in society. The group rules are extraordinarily rigid and malefactors are treated to group anger, vituperation and sometimes to such punishments as having their heads shaved. Of the approximately 2,000 persons admitted to the program, all of whom must be volunteers, approximately half have left Synanon without completing the therapeutic course. Of the others, the overwhelming majority remain in residence in one of the several Synanon centers. The total number who have returned to the community is not known but appears to range between 100 and 200. Thus, in a ten-year period, an average of no more than twenty persons per year has been returned to the community drug-free, and even for these the follow-up data are currently inadequate. This is not meant to derogate the Synanon approach; of those who remain in residence, many are performing constructive activities in the numerous Synanon business ventures, such as gasoline stations. However, it is important to recognize that one must be extremely well motivated to tolerate the inordinately rigid inpatient residential program. Even those who start out well motivated often cannot maintain it, as indicated by the 50 per cent drop-out rate. Thus Synanon may well speak to the needs of a small number of addicts, but it is highly unlikely to be applicable at a public health level in solving the heroin addiction problem in this country.

Daytop Lodge and Village constitutes an offshoot of Synanon, with certain important differences. It has two facilities, one in Staten Island, New York, and the other in a rural setting in Sullivan County, New York, the current patient capacity being some two hundred persons. Founded in 1963, Daytop accepts not only volunteers but also those referred on probation by the courts. The residential program, structured like Synanon's, is almost as rigid. Gradually, the individual, who is forbidden to use drugs of any sort, is allowed to progress upward in the hierarchy, at each step assuming more responsibility within the group. Continually, each person engages in confrontations with other members of the group; in abrasively frank fashion, defenses are stripped away, the individual is forced to face reality, and attempts are made through this catharsis to achieve maturity. In Daytop, an increasingly popular form of group therapy is the so-called marathon, a thirty-hour session in which ten to fifteen people confront each other virtually continuously, hoping that when the participants become physically and mentally exhausted, heretofore impenetrable defense mechanisms will collapse. Unlike Synanon, which has no clearly established goals of returning the addict to the community, Daytop prepares its residents for discharge after a one and one-half year inpatient period. During 1965 and 1966, 303 individuals entered Daytop Village but of these, almost half left the program without completing the course of therapy. As of June, 1969, only one hundred had completed the program and were considered successfully rehabilitated, and the majority of these remain either in staff positions with Daytop or are in other anti-addiction programs. Thus Daytop too must be considered in its nascent stages. Although those within the program are fiercely loyal to its objectives and achievements, it is far too early to make even a preliminary judgment as to its efficacy or the percentage of addicts to which this approach might be appropriately applied.

In the early 1960s Dr. Efren Ramirez, who until recently was coordinator of addiction programs for the City of New York, carried out in Puerto Rico an experimental program characterized by three separate phases. The first phase, called induction, consists of attempts to reach out into the community to the addict population, and then, on a voluntary outpatient basis to inculcate motivation in such a way that the addict is willing to accept detoxification and withdrawal from drugs. If he is willing, the addict is then placed in a second phase consisting of treatment in a therapeutic community for an average of six to eight months; here, under psychiatric guidance, attempts are made by group and individual therapy to induce behavioral changes that will allow the patient to commit himself to a long-term rehabilitative program. During the third phase the ex-addict is reintroduced gradually into community responsibilities.

In the Puerto Rican program a total of 1,800 individuals were contacted, of whom 700 actually became involved in the program; 125 of these completed treatment and for them the relapse rate, with a three-year follow-up, is said to be less than 5 per cent. This program, too, appears to offer considerable promise, but it is important to emphasize that only 40 per cent of those who initially showed an interest in the program ever became involved and that less than 10 per cent of those originally contacted actually had completed the three stages. Furthermore, even for those who are considered successfully rehabilitated, follow-up data in some areas remain fragmentary and inadequate.

The current program of the Addiction Services Agency in New York City is an offshoot of the Ramirez program. It too has not returned enough addicts to the community to make any judgment about its efficiency.

In 1961, the California legislature established a civil commitment program for narcotic addicts. The treatment program is carried out at the massive, monolithic California Rehabilitation Center in Corona, which is situated sixty-five miles outside Los Angeles and has a bed capacity for nineteen hundred men and four hundred women. Each person committed is placed in a living unit composed of either sixty men or fifty women. The emphasis is on daily group therapy, which is guided by staff members who have various amounts of training in psychiatry, psychology, sociology or penology. There are some educational and vocational training programs but these are limited in scope. Once the individual is released he is kept under careful supervision by a parole officer whose caseload has been maintained at a maximum of thirty. The California program is in many ways very rigid. If an individual volunteers for treatment, he may be kept under supervision for a maximum of two and one-half years, but if he is committed by a relative or through the courts, he is under supervision for seven years, a period that can be extended for an additional three years if the addict has a relapse. Thus for possession of a small amount of heroin, for example, an individual may fall under the aegis of the state for up to ten years, an extraordinarily long period of time for that particular offense. Data through 1969 show that approximately one third of those released from the Corona facility and given outpatient status have maintained their freedom, whereas two thirds have been returned to the rehabilitation center.

Although the initial figures look rather discouraging, the rigidity of the program may be in part responsible for the low recovery rate. Once granted outpatient status, an individual can be returned to the Corona Rehabilitation Center for drug use, for drinking, for fighting or even for refusing to get a job. Many feel the outpatient supervision is the most important aspect of the California program and that there is little evidence the group therapy sessions in the massive Corona center are really very effective.

Never before has such a massive attack been mounted against addiction as is taking place in New York State under the administration of Governor Nelson Rockefeller. During the first year, starting in April, 1967, over 250 million dollars were spent to construct and rehabilitate facilities, obtain adequate personnel and initiate treatment programs. In subsequent years the carrying charges of the program are likely to run between forty and eighty million dollars yearly. Addicts may reach the program in a variety of ways. They may apply for admission after arrest and before trial, or those convicted of narcotic-related misdemeanors may be referred to the program by the judge, as may those convicted of certain felonies. Others may volunteer, or may be involuntarily committed even if they are not charged with a crime. Those addicts volunteering, involuntarily committed or committed prior to trial or after conviction for a misdemeanor are under state supervision for a period of up to three years; convicted felons are under supervision for up to five years. The involuntary civil commitment for those who have not been charged with a crime has been seriously challenged by civil libertarians, who maintain it breaches constitutional guarantees. But even if this provision should eventually be eliminated, the program is capable of reaching the majority of addicts in New York State. During inpatient residence at a variety of facilities throughout the state, the addict will be treated with group and individual psychotherapy, in addition to which there are major projects relating to educational and vocational training. Furthermore, vocational training will continue during the outpatient period in halfway houses and in the community. Vigorous efforts will be made not only to place the addicts in available jobs, but also to reorient community thinking so that the ex-addicts will be accepted and given equal opportunity in the job market. Perhaps most important of all, the New York program will spend well over a million dollars a year in intensive, preventive education, using talks, motion pictures, pamphlets, etc., in an attempt to reach every high school and college student in areas in which drug abuse of any sort is indigenous. Additionally, millions of dollars will be spent both within the program itself and in extramural contracts to permit the testing of a variety of experimental approaches including methadone maintenance, treatment with narcotic antagonists, group and individual psychotherapy programs, and indeed any other therapeutic approach or combination of approaches which appears to be promising. Built into the program is a rigid evaluation mechanism, so that in a period of several years it will be possible to determine which of the many experimental projects hold most promise for widespread application at a public health level. As in the California program, the ex-addict will be closely supervised once he returns to the community in the hope this will help him remain drug-free. Since this program is in its early phases, it is far too early to make even a preliminary judgment, but it stands as the best-funded, most flexible, most comprehensive program ever undertaken in an attempt to rehabilitate existing addicts and by education to prevent others from becoming involved in the depravity and degradation characteristic of heroin abuse.

These then are the six major programs in the treatment of heroin addiction; in addition, there are a substantial number of others which either are similar to one or more of those discussed above or are limited to a relatively small number of addicts. Of the six, excellent results are already claimed for the methadone program, Synanon, Daytop and the Ramirez approach. Recognizing that each program has its limitations and remains in the research state, it is nevertheless intriguing that such diverse approaches as methadone blockade, the Synanon/Daytop abrasive techniques of group therapy, and a psychiatrically dominated program such as Dr. Ramirez' all report similarly enthusiastic results. Talks with addicts in each of the four projects reveal a fierce loyalty and pride concerning that particular program, and therein, I believe, lies the secret of their potential success. It seems to me that it does not matter whether one treats with drugs, emphasizes psychiatry or depends on non-medically oriented group therapy. What does matter is that the addict—immature, angry, frustrated, rejected and rejecting—becomes committed to something. Once he achieves that commitment to a program or to a group, he is well on his way toward achieving a drug-free life. For volunteers such commitment must come from within; whereas in the California and New York State programs the compulsory nature of the civil commitment hopefully will be able to impose such commitment externally. It seems clear that for the majority of addicts, who are basically poorly motivated, a program such as that initiated in New York State, with mandatory supervisory aspects, has the greatest chance for success; for the well-motivated addict who wishes to be cured, the choice among a variety of programs may be very useful. Of course, the real answer to heroin addiction is not rehabilitation but prevention; and it will require an enormous effort to reduce the supply of heroin, educate the potentially susceptible and attack the underlying urban problems which spawn opiate abuse.

CHAPTER ELEVEN

THE FUTURE—
PROBLEMS AND RECOMMENDATIONS

There are obviously no facile answers to the burgeoning problems contributing to, and resulting from, indiscriminate and promiscuous use of drugs. Many of the problems are rooted in much larger questions facing our society. But perhaps it would be useful to discuss some of the specific areas in which real progress can be made on a hard practical basis in the next few years, and at the same time to indicate some of the new problems that may arise. Drug abuse must not be regarded as an entity in and of itself but rather as a manifestation of some underlying abnormality, either in the individual or in society. Unless we accept the fact that illicit drug use is a consequence of personal or sociological defects, it will be impossible to make an intelligent attack on the basic causes—and thus reduce the problem in the most effective and lasting fashion, by preventing it. Far better preventive education programs must be formulated and promulgated. Anti-drug education directed at young people must be carried out cautiously because of the undeniable risk that in some it will merely create a morbid curiosity. Done carefully, utilizing pamphlets, motion pictures and vigorous speakers, who relate well to a young audience, preventive education programs can be highly beneficial, especially with the more dangerous drugs such as the stimulants, heroin and potent hallucinogens such as LSD. Even the growing marihuana problem can be attacked with preventive education, although here the results are likely to be far less dramatic. Indeed, perhaps the most important function of education regarding marihuana is to de-glamorize the drug by pointing out that the kick is small and that marihuana's lure for many people is sociological—not pharmacological—in that it symbolizes revolt, defiance and rejection of society's established mores. It is also important to stress that the marihuana problem cannot be considered by itself but must be evaluated in the context of more potent and potentially more toxic forms of cannabis as well as other pleasure-giving drugs such as amphetamines which may become candidates for legalization.

Educational programs must also be directed to teachers and parents; unless these individuals understand the nature of the problems, they will be of little help to their children and students. It should be stressed that educational programs and individual speakers must be scrupulously honest and factual. If an over-zealous lecturer, for example, states that marihuana leads to lung cancer or that it inevitably impels the user to turn to more potent drugs, he is almost certain to undermine his credibility, and end by actually performing a disservice.

The question always arises as to which school grades should receive anti-drug indoctrination. My own feeling is that junior high school classes should be exposed to the general problems of excessive use of drugs. Then at the high school level, problems relating to specific drugs such as hallucinogens, stimulants or opiates could be considered in detail. In view of the current increasing use of marihuana and stimulant pills in junior high schools, it might be necessary in certain schools to initiate educational efforts on specific drugs at that level.

It seems almost inevitable, though, that the use of marihuana will continue to grow so long as the drug is glamorized and is held emblematic of revolt by restless young people living in an inordinately permissive society devoted increasingly to its own pleasure. Indeed, it seems likely that within the next two to three years, in many areas of the country, a majority of college and perhaps even of high school students will have at least experimented with marihuana—although as long as the drug remains illegal, it *is* unlikely that more than 20 per cent will become involved with either chronic or heavy use.

Educational institutions must not ignore their responsibilities in this regard. Once regulations are established in regard to drugs, each institution must demand obedience, or it will encourage not only drug use but also a form of irresponsibility which inevitably will interfere with the learning process. More and more schools and colleges are adopting a firm but fair approach. Harvard College took the most publicized step in the spring of 1967. Their brief memorandum to the freshman class said, "As anyone bright enough to be at Harvard knows perfectly well, possession or distribution of marihuana and LSD is strictly against the law and taking drugs involves users in psychological dangers and contacts with the criminal underworld. The college is prepared to take serious disciplinary action up to and including dismissal against any student found to be involved in use or distribution of illegal and dangerous drugs. In sum, if a student is stupid enough to misuse his time here fooling around with illegal and dangerous drugs, our view is that he should leave college and make room for people prepared to take good advantage of the college opportunity."

To dismiss a student and thereby endanger his entire future is indeed a harsh penalty, but the obligation of schools and colleges is to consider the health of the community at large; to allow illicit drug users to remain active is to court disaster, in that they may well attempt to subvert as many of their classmates as possible. The Harvard approach is firm but allows the administration flexibility in dealing with each individual case.

Despite the need for a firm approach it is clear caution must be exercised in regard to entrapment within our schools and universities. There is absolutely no reason for the college campus to be inviolate if students are disobeying the laws by illicit use or distribution of dangerous drugs, but by the same token it would be tragic if the drug problems in our educational institutions were compounded by paranoia relating to undercover agents within the student body. Since it stands to reason that the campus cannot be sacrosanct for the drug pusher, a reasonable compromise might mandate that the school administration always be informed of the presence of undercover agents and that the function of those agents be strictly limited to ferreting out and punishing those who are clearly involved in the sale of drugs. Although detection and arrest of users of drugs such as heroin and marihuana is also a police function, entrapment of users by undercover agents within the university environment would create far more problems than it would solve.

Whenever possible, much of the responsibility for coping with the illicit use of drugs in educational institutions should be delegated to student council organizations, since in both high schools and colleges student representatives are usually well motivated and highly responsible. They know the drug users as well as the drug proselytizers, and they are far more knowledgeable in this regard than any school administration. If they themselves will accept the responsibility for discouraging drug use on campus, the extent of abuse within those environments will rapidly diminish.

The control of drugs on campus in the next few years is liable to be considerably affected by an inevitable change in the tenor of the marihuana debate, a change caused by the availability of tetrahydrocannabinol. Even now there are illicit chemists synthesizing the material; within a short time the market is likely to be flooded with a variety of cannabinol derivatives. Although synthesis of tetrahydrocannabinol is now easy to perform, the substance has exhibited marked instability, deteriorating on exposure to air at room temperature. This accounts for its nonavailability on the illicit market now. However, it is likely the problem of instability will soon be solved. The effects of the synthetic material will be far different from those resulting from smoking one or even several marihuana cigarettes. The mental effects of cannabis are largely dose-related. If one uses small amounts, psychosis, depression, panic or mental deterioration is relatively unlikely, whereas if the dose is large enough, virtually every user develops a psychotic reaction not unlike that seen with LSD. The marihuana cigarette imposes its own dose limitations, but once the synthetic material is available it will be possible to take as large a dose as one wishes. Inevitably, some people will start with extraordinarily large doses; others, who take small amounts initially and enjoy the effects, will progress to larger and larger amounts. Under these circumstances, the reaction rate will rise substantially. Those who continue to insist that marihuana is innocuous will then be faced squarely with the realities of the dosage phenomenon. It will become abundantly clear that when taken in substantial doses cannabis is indeed a potentially dangerous drug. Once that happens the main prop under the legalize-marihuana argument will be destroyed and inevitably much of the fervor behind the marihuana movement will disappear.

Clearly, the drug laws must be modified. The possession of marihuana or other cannabis preparations, even in amounts large enough to make twenty-five to fifty cigarettes, should be construed as a relatively minor crime. Cannabis offense should fall under the dangerous drug laws and not the narcotic laws. For at least the first two offenses, conviction on possession charges should carry a constructive sentence, as for instance, assignment to a local anti-poverty program for an appropriate period of time. Additionally, it should be provided that upon completion of that sentence the conviction be expunged from the record, so as not to affect the individual's future deleteriously. If, of course, the individual continued to violate the cannabis possession laws, there would be no recourse but to incarcerate him, but even then the maximum sentence should never exceed six months. Such changes in the posession laws would not legitimatize, legalize or condone the use of marihuana, but they would make the penalty consistent with the nature of the crime, and by so doing they would take a great deal of the steam out of the current overblown debate. Furthermore, laws regarding merely visiting a place where marihuana is being used or dispensed should be repealed. At the same time, it should be recognized that there is no need to change the current penalties for importing, selling or distributing marihuana or other cannabis products.

On the other hand, the laws regarding potent and dangerous hallucinogens such as LSD and STP should be stiff. At both the state and the federal level, possession of these drugs should be a misdemeanor, and sale, manufacture or smuggling should be a felony. Equally important, giving these drugs to an individual without his knowledge, a reprehensible offense, should clearly be a felony. In regard to dispensing drugs such as LSD or STP without cost, the laws should provide the judiciary with the flexibility to give misdemeanor sentences to those who merely shared small amounts, and felony sentences to those who appear to be major proselytizers. These recommendations may appear stringent but the potential risks to the individual and to society as well as the messianic nature of the hallucinogenic zealots demand vigorous and firm laws and regulations.

On a larger scale, the whole structure of our dangerous drug laws should be revised to accommodate three categories: (A) more dangerous drugs (B) an intermediate group and (C) less dangerous drugs. The less dangerous category, which might include for example codeine, would incur potential penalties for possession ranging from a mere reprimand to a modest fine or at most a jail sentence of a maximum of thirty days; sale, manufacture or smuggling might carry a maximum sentence of one year in jail. Marihuana would be included in the intermediate group in which penalty provisions would be similar to those outlined above for cannabis. The penalties would be greater in the more dangerous category, possession being a misdemeanor, and sale, manufacture or smuggling being a felony. Flexibility should be built into the laws so that if drug fads change or new dangers become apparent, drugs can be shifted by administrative fiat from one category to another. Were such a law enacted, it would seem at present that amphetamines, for example, or other central-stimulant pills for ingestion by mouth, should be placed in the intermediate group, whereas methamphetamine in the crystalline or liquid form suited to the far more dangerous intravenous use of the drug, should be placed in the more dangerous category. If the pills should be used, as in Sweden, to make suspensions for intravenous injection, this form, too, could be placed in the more dangerous category.

Such flexibility is important particularly in respect to the development of new drug fads. Central stimulants, in fact, in the form of such drugs as Methedrine, Ritalin and Preludin, may very likely be the next major fad. The use of these drugs will be furthered not by their stimulant effects per se, but rather by the belief that they can be used for aphrodisiac purposes. The data from the Swedish experience are now appearing in the literature in Europe and, unavoidably, the reports valid or apocryphal, that central stimulants increase interest in sex and augment performance will reach the United States. In a society hung up on sex, this suggestion alone is bound to stimulate an enormous interest in this category of drugs. However, it is likely to be only a passing fad. For one thing, when the drug is taken by mouth, even in large doses, its sexual effects, even for one oriented in that direction, are unpredictable. If the central stimulants are indeed aphrodisiacs, which is open to question, their effect is most noted if the drug is given intravenously, and this fact will automatically limit the prevalence of abuse. Also, prolonged heavy use of central stimulants frequently has sexual effects diametrically opposite to the ones desired. At this stage, intercourse may no longer appear pleasurable even though the individual engages in it frequently, orgasm may be inhibited completely and in males impotence may develop. Furthermore, those who use central stimulants heavily are likely to find that on discontinuing the drugs, sexual activity will not appear either meaningful or enjoyable for a long period of time. Finally, the complication rate and the number of undesirable side effects is enormous; paranoid psychosis, accidents, brain damage (possibly permanent) and a high incidence of hepatitis. The greatest danger for society is that the combination of increased energy, decreased inhibitions, and paranoia, in a traditionally violent society, will produce a high incidence of aggressive activity. None of these possibilities will dissuade young people from experimentation and even heavy use, but the complications are such that society is likely to react vigorously and repressively, and the discovery that stimulant use does not automatically transform people into sexual athletes will eventually reduce the incidence of abuse.

In addition to the strong possibility that central stimulants will be our next major drug problem, it seems likely that many drug users will experiment with virtually any agent with intoxication potential. In the past there was little overlap between groups using LSD, heroin and amphetamines. Now some individuals who start with marihuana try not only LSD and stimulants, but also heroin. Even among our college population there is some heroin experimentation and increasing reports of students who, initiated into the world of drug use by smoking marihuana, experimented transiently with potent hallucinogens and oral stimulants and then became intravenous Methedrine habitués.

Part of the tendency to experiment with many drugs is related to ebullient reports about new agents promulgated by the drug cult; such statements are almost always accompanied by assurances of the new agents' safety. Thus, for example, in the spring of 1967, Dr. Leary pronounced the prolonged psychedelic effects and safety of STP and Asthmador, the latter a readily available proprietary preparation with legitimate medical uses when used under appropriate circumstances. STP, chemically 2,5 dimethoxy-4-methyl-amphetamine, is closely related to mescaline and amphetamine. It was studied carefully by Drs. Solomon Snyder, Louis Faillace and Leo Hollister who, reporting in *Science* (November 3, 1967), found the drug produced vivid hallucinations and had a similar duration of action to LSD. However Drs. J. Robertson Unwin, Lionel P. Solursh and Wilfred R. Clement, summarizing the street experience with the drug in the Canadian Medical Association *Journal* (February 24, 1968), emphasized STP's immense toxicity; they noted prolonged manic psychoses lasting several days, blurred vision, fever, difficulty swallowing and instances of death from respiratory failure or convulsions. In three cases, Thorazine, the most reliable antidote for LSD was administered and this precipitated cardiovascular collapse. Others have reported that Thorazine also accentuates strikingly the manic psychoses of STP. Allegedly twenty thousand STP capsules were distributed free at a love-in at Golden Gate Park in San Francisco. For a brief period STP was used with abandon, but this particular fad diminished quickly when its adverse effects became evident.

Asthmador, which contains stramonium and belladonna alkaloids, is also highly toxic when ingested injudiciously. The toxic manifestations, described in some 20 cases by Dr. Daniel Teitelbaum in the January, 1968 *Annals of Internal Medicine*, include agitation, frightening visions, stupor and coma.

Severe toxicity is not likely to deter proselytizers from uncritically extolling new agents. Indeed, as the fears of LSD grow it is likely that psychedelic proponents will urge use not only of new agents but also of already available ones such as psilocybin, peyote, and dimethyltryptamine, even though the evidence suggests administration of these drugs will be associated with LSD-like toxicity. Furthermore, there is an increasing tendency to use combinations of drugs in a single capsule; two popular combinations have been LSD and Methedrine, and mescaline, LSD and cocaine. More and more the user has very little idea of the actual contents of pills or capsules he ingests, and this complicates the medical treatment if toxicity occurs.

The continual development of new drugs also obviously greatly complicates the problems of legal control. Just laws and properly adjusted penalties can only grow out of a continuing dialogue on drugs between the judiciary, the legislative branches, law enforcement agencies and medical societies. Too often the judges treat pushers and sellers as if they were users, and demonstrate inadequate knowledge of the intricacies of the drug racket. Sometimes even the most venal criminals who were not addicted themselves but made enormous profits in the heroin business have been given surprisingly light sentences. If the supply of dangerous drugs is to be reduced, the penalties meted out to the smugglers, distributors and pushers, especially of opiates and potent hallucinogens, must be very severe. Furthermore it seems to me some form of carefully controlled wiretapping should be permitted for cases of illicit importation, sale, manufacture or distribution of dangerous drugs including heroin, potent hallucinogens and central stimulants of the intravenous variety. There is absolutely no reason for our society not to be able to come to grips with the question of how to protect itself from criminal elements and at the same time protect the individual from excessive interference with his privacy. It would also be helpful if every state medical society formally established a subcommittee whose sole function was to keep abreast of the medical aspects of dangerous drugs and to be at all times available to governmental officials, to the judiciary and to the communications media. If the newspapers as well as television and radio were aware of it, they might, when new drug fads arise, become accustomed to making inquiry before making public pronouncements which are uncritical and injudicious and which augment the problem. In the nascent phases of abuse, the alleged glories of a new drug could then be adequately balanced by reports and information concerning potential dangers.

Clearly the Congress of the United States must at long last accept its true responsibilities in the field of drug abuse by providing far more in the way of funds both to local enforcement agencies and to those organizations attempting rehabilitation. Public pronouncements notwithstanding, the amount of funds currently available is grossly inadequate. In order to spend public monies wisely, it is imperative that all rehabilitation programs for drug abuses should undergo extramural evaluation before being considered potential candidates for widespread application. Too often the ebullient reports of various programs are widely publicized in the press and are accepted uncritically by those in a position to transform them into public health policy. Some form of careful scrutiny is necessary to separate enthusiasm from fact and hopes from valid accomplishments. Unless this is done we will continue to invest enormous amounts of money and emotion in programs which are fundamentally, for one reason or another, nonviable. It is equally important that the public, as well as legislators and those in the executive branch adopt an attitude of patience in regard to new and possibly important programs. Any major program requires at least a year to get into full swing and an additional two years to produce results. There are no facile or instantaneous cures for drug abuse. To attempt to subvert a potentially excellent program before it is permitted even to become fully established is clearly a disservice to the public.

Beyond rehabilitation programs there must be community acceptance of the ex-drug user. Once a person has stopped using drugs and his rehabilitation has been initiated, it is crucial for him to be able to return to the community with equal opportunities to live and work. If communities will not accept ex-addicts on such terms, no medical and sociologic rehabilitation program can be successful. At present, at least in regard to heroin addiction, this is a major problem. For example, in many localities restrictions remain for the ex-addict in regard to barber's, beautician's and even driver's licenses. These must be removed. Community acceptance does not, of course, assure the success of any rehabilitation program, but community rejection guarantees its failure.

However, the drug abuse problem in deprived urban areas will not be solved until a vigorous attack is made on urban blight. The United States Congress as well as state and local governments appear at present incapable of dealing effectively with this, the greatest domestic problem facing the country. So long as people, especially those of ethnically deprived minorities, are compelled to endure poor education, inadequate housing and lack of jobs and recreational opportunities, a variety of antisocial activities will persist, among them drug abuse. If our dilapidated urban slums disappeared, 70 to 80 per cent of the heroin problem would go with them.

In both deprived and affluent areas, parents and teachers must work together to get young people committed. Many young people have a chronic identity problem. This, more than anything else, is the essential ingredient in any attack on the drug problem. Those who are committed to scholastic achievement, extracurricular activities, the community or a variety of other constructive projects, may still experiment with a less dangerous drug such as marihuana, but it is far less likely that they will experiment with more dangerous drugs or will become chronic users of even the mildest of the illicitly used drugs.

In the long run, attempts to achieve commitment in young people must be accompanied by a concerted effort to increase family strength. This can be achieved in part by up-grading family courts and family counseling services. Additionally, massive educational campaigns must be undertaken to bring home to parents the effects on their children of their own injudicious behavior or indiscriminate use of drugs. A desire for commitment and realization of the importance of family strength must be inculcated into our children during their formative school years. This can be accomplished both by formal courses and by less-formal techniques, but whatever the methods, they must be implemented far more effectively than they are now.

Although it is clear many new mind-altering drugs will be available in the future, it is impossible to predict how they will be used. T. J. Gordon, of Douglas Aircraft, has suggested that "perhaps tomorrow we will have the pharmaceutical equivalent of the liquor store in which chemicals can be obtained to buy any mood from euphoria to mystic contemplation. Wives perhaps will slip anti-grouch pills into their husband's morning coffee." The dangers inherent in permitting mind-altering drugs to become integral parts of our daily routine are obviously enormous, but within the next two decades mood-control may shift from chemicals to electrical mediators. Electrodes can be precisely implanted in certain areas of the brain, and experimental animals or people can literally be turned on to pleasure. Gordon cites a study in which a rat was wired so that it could achieve what apparently was a pleasurable sensation merely by pecking at a button. The animal became so pleasure-oriented that it would press the button 8,000 times an hour and stop only because of exhaustion or for food.

Obviously the illicit use of drugs is sometimes a manifestation of a sick, insecure, angry or unhappy personality. At other times, especially concerning drugs such as marihuana, use represents only a brief fling by exuberant and intemperate youths; dire implications should not be read in such transgressions. Recurrent or chronic illicit use of drugs, however, is often a reflection of our troubled society—a society in which respect for the laws is disdained, which at least temporarily appears to have lost the capacity to make its visions a reality, which appears to be dominated by a technology it cannot or will not control, and in which idealism and achievement appear to have been subverted by an ever-quickening rush to sensate pleasures. Laws can be passed, preventive education undertaken, and millions spent on rehabilitation, but until this society regains its vigor, direction and integrity, the promiscuous, indiscriminate and illicit use of mind-altering and other dangerous drugs will remain a major problem.

GLOSSARY OF TERMS

acid   LSD
artillery   equipment for injecting drugs
bad scene   a situation likely to result in unpleasant drug experience or other types of trouble
back up (back track)   to allow blood to come back into the syringe during intravenous injection
bale   a pound of marihuana
ball   to have a good experience, especially a sexual one
bang   to inject drugs
bennies   amphetamines
big c   cocaine
blasted   to be intoxicated by a drug
blow one's mind   to break with personal reality
blow a stick   to smoke a marihuana cigarette
blue heavens   amytal
blue velvet   a combination of paregoric and antihistamine for intravenous use
bombita (bombito)   amphetamine for injection
boo   marihuana
boost   to shoplift
bummer   an unpleasant drug experience
busted   to be arrested
can   approximately an ounce of marihuana
candy   cocaine
cap   a packet of heroin
cartwheels   amphetamines
Charlie   cocaine
Christmas trees   tuinal (secobarbital and amobarbital)
coke   cocaine

cold turkey   an abrupt withdrawal from narcotics without medication

come down   the ending of a drug experience

cooker   a receptacle in which drugs are heated prior to intravenous injection

cool   to be in tune with the modern scene; to handle life situations in a satisfactory manner

cop out   to withdraw

crystals   a crystalline form of methamphetamine (Methedrine)

cut   to adulterate with a variety of materials including milk sugar

dealer   a seller of drugs

deck   a packet of heroin

dexies   dexedrine

dime bag $10 worth of drugs

dolly   methadone (dolophine)

drop   to take pills or capsules by mouth

fix   an injection of narcotics

flip out   to lose mental and/or emotional control following use of drugs, especially powerful hallucinogens

freak out   same as above

floating   to be intoxicated

footballs   a combination of dextroamphetamine and amphetamine

fuzz   the police, or federal agents

gin   cocaine

give wings   to inject somebody with heroin by vein or to teach a person to inject the heroin himself

goofballs   barbiturates

grass   marihuana

H   heroin

hash   hashish

hay   marihuana

head (pothead, acid head)   one high as much of the time as possible on LSD, marihuana, or hashish

heavenly blues   a type of morning-glory seeds

high   to be under the influence of drugs

hooked   to be dependent on drugs, usually meaning addiction to heroin

horse   heroin

hung up   to be enmeshed in personal problems, usually of a psychological nature

hustle   to be a prostitute

joint   marihuana cigarette

joy pop   the intermittent use of heroin by a nonaddict

junkie   a narcotic addict

kick the habit   to stop using drugs

lid   approximately 1 ounce of marihuana

lit up   to be under the influence of drugs

main-line   to take drugs directly intravenously

(the) man   police

Maryjane   marihuana

meth   methamphetamine as liquid or in crystalline form

methheads   chronic and heavy users of Methedrine

nemmies   nembutal

nickel bag   a $5 supply of drugs

nod   to behave in a lethargic manner, if not a somnolent one, when under the influence of drugs, usually narcotic

OD   overdose of narcotics, often lethal

pack   a packet of heroin

panic   a scarcity of drugs

pearly gates   a type of morning-glory seeds

pot   marihuana

purple hearts   phenobarbital (luminal)

pusher   a seller of drugs

put on   to deceive or confuse intentionally

rainbows   tuinal (amobarbital and secobarbital)

red birds, red devils, reds   seconal

reefer   marihuana cigarette

roach   marihuana cigarette butt

score   to obtain drugs

shoot   to take drugs by needle

shooting gallery   a place where narcotics are used in injection

skin pop   to inject drugs under the skin

smack   heroin

snipe   marihuana cigarette butt

snort   to take drugs by sniffing through the nose

snow   cocaine

speed ball   heroin together with cocaine or amphetamine

speed freak   one constantly high on amphetamines

spike   a needle used for injecting drugs

split   to leave or run away

spoon   a measure of drug to be injected, usually referring to about 1 gram of amphetamines

stash   to hide illegal drugs

stick   marihuana cigarette

stoned   to be high on drugs

sweeties   Preludin (British term)

tea   marihuana

teeny-bopper   a teenage hippie out for kicks

tooies   tuinal (secobarbital and amobarbital)

trip   an hallucinogenic experience usually involving LSD

turned off   to have lost interest or enthusiasm for something

turned on   to be excited or enthralled by something, often drugs; almost always refers to a sensory experience

twenty-five   LSD

weed   marihuana

wired   to be addicted or habituated

yellow jackets   nembutal (pentobarbital)

BIBLIOGRAPHY

BOOKS AND MONOGRAPHS

Abramson, Harold A. (ed.). *The Use of LSD in Psychotherapy and Alcoholism*. New York and Indianapolis: The Bobbs-Merrill Co., Inc., 1967.

American Bar Association and American Medical Association. *Drug Addiction: Crime or Disease?* Bloomington, Indiana: Indiana University Press, 1961.

Bischoff, W. H. *The Ecstasy Drugs*. Delray Beach, Florida: University Circle Press, 1966.

Braden, William. *The Private Sea: LSD and the Search for God*. Chicago: Quadrangle Books, 1967.

Chein, I., D. L. Gerard, R. S. Lee and E. Rosenfeld. *The Road to H*. New York: Basic Books, Inc., 1964.

Cohen, Sidney. *The Beyond Within: The LSD Story*. New York: Atheneum Publishers, 1964.

Connell, P. H. *Amphetamine Psychosis*. London: Chapman and Hall, Ltd., 1958.

DeBold, R. C. and R. C. Leaf (eds.). *LSD Man & Society*. Middletown, Connecticut: Wesleyan University Press, 1967.

Efron, P. H. *Ethnopharmacologic Search for Psychoactive Drugs*. United States Public Health Service, Publication No. 1645. Washington: Government Printing Office, 1967.

Eldridge, W. B. *Narcotics and the Law*. Chicago: American Bar Foundation, 1962.

Goldstein, Richard. *One of Seven: Drugs on Campus*. New York: Walker and Co., 1966.

Huxley, Aldous. *The Doors of Perception, and Heaven and Hell*. New York: Harper & Row, Publishers, Inc., 1954.

Keniston, Kenneth. *The Uncommitted: Alienated Youth in American Society*. New York: Dell Publishing Co., 1967.

Kolb, L. *Drug Addiction.* Springfield, Illinois: Charles C. Thomas, 1962.

Laurie, Peter. *Drugs: Medical, Psychological and Social Facts.* Baltimore, Maryland: Penguin Books, 1967.

Lindesmith, A. R. *Opiate Addiction.* Elsah, Illinois: The Principia Press.

Maurer, D. W. and V. H. Vogel. *Narcotics and Narcotic Addiction.* Springfield, Illinois: Charles C. Thomas, 1962.

Mayor's Committee on Marihuana. *The Marihuana Problem in the City of New York.* Lancaster, Pennsylvania: Jacques Cattrell Press, 1944. (also available in Solomon, *The Marihuana Papers,* see below.

Schur, Edwin M. *Narcotic Addiction in Britain and America.* Bloomington, Indiana: Indiana University Press, 1963.

Simmons, J. L. and B. Winograd. *It's Happening.* Santa Barbara, California: Marc-Laird Publications, 1967.

Smith, Kline and French Laboratories. *Drug Abuse: Escape to Nowhere.* 1967.

Solomon, David. *The Marihuana Papers.* New York and Indianapolis: The Bobbs-Merrill Company, Inc., 1966.

Taylor, Norman. *Narcotics: Nature's Dangerous Gifts.* New York: Dell Publishing Co., 1963.

Weil, G. M., R. Metzner and T. Leary. *The Psychedelic Reader.* New Hyde Park, New York: University Books, 1965.

IMPORTANT ARTICLES

Allentuck, S. and K. M. Bowman. "The Psychiatric Aspects of Marihuana Intoxication," *American Journal of Psychiatry,* Vol. 99 (1942), 248.

Barron, F., M. E. Jarvik and S. Brunnell. "The Hallucinogenic Drugs," *Scientific American,* Vol. 210 (1964), 29.

Benabud, A. "Psycho-pathological Aspect of the Cannabis Situation in Morocco," *United Nations Bulletin on Narcotics,* Vol. 9, No. 4 (1957), 1.

Bromberg, W. "Marihuana: A Psychiatric Study," *Journal of the American Medical Association,* Vol. 113 (1939), 4.

Chopra, I. C. and R. N. Chopra. "The Use of Cannibis Drugs in India," *United Nations Bulletin on Narcotics,* Vol. 9, No. 1 (1957), 4.

Cohen, S. and K. S. Ditman. "Complications Associated with Lysergic Acid Diethylamide (LSD-25)," *Journal of the American Medical Association*, Vol. 181 (1962), 161-162.

Dole, V. P. and M. Nyswander. "Medical Treatment for Diacetylmorphine (heroin) Addiction: A Clinical Trial with Methadone hydrochloride," *Journal of the American Medical Association*, Vol. 193 (1965), 646.

Frosch, W. A., E. Robbins, L. Robbins, and M. Stern. "Motivation for Self-Administration of LSD," *Psychiatric Quarterly* (January, 1967).

Halleck, S. L. "Psychiatric Treatment of the Alienated College Student," *American Journal of Psychiatry*, Vol. 124 (November, 1967), 642.

Hoffer, A. "D-lysergic acid diethylamide (LSD). Review of Its Present Status," *Clinical Pharmacology and Therapeutics*, Vol. 6 (1965), 183.

Huxley, A. "The History of Tension," *Annals of the New York Academy of Science*, Vol. 67 (May, 1957), 675-684.

Isbell, H., C. W. Gorodetzsky and D. Jasinski. "Effects of (-)A⁹ Trans tetrahydrocannabinol in Man," *Psychopharmacologia*, Vol. 11 (1967), 184-188.

Keeler, M. H. "Adverse Reaction to Marihuana," *American Journal of Psychiatry*, Vol. 124 (Nov. 1967), 674.

Kramer, J. C., V. S. Fischman and D. C. Littlefield. "Amphetamine Abuse: Pattern and Effects of High Doses taken Intravenously," *Journal of the American Medical Association*, Vol. 201 (July 31, 1967), 305.

Kurland, A. A., S. Unger, J. W. Shaffer and C. Savage. "Psychedelic Therapy Utilizing LSD in the Treatment of the Alcoholic Patient," *American Journal of Psychiatry*, Vol. 123 (1967), 1202-1209.

Larimore, G. W. and H. Brill. "The British Narcotic System," *New York State Journal of Medicine*, Vol. 60 (1960), 107.

Leary, T. "Interview," *Playboy*, Vol. 13 (Sept., 1966). 93.

Loughman, W. D., T. W. Sargent and D. M. Israelstam. "Leukocytes of Humans Exposed to Lysergic Acid Diethylamide: Lack of Chromosomal Damage," *Science*, Vol. 158 (October, 1967), 508-510.

Louria, D. B. "Current Concepts: Lysergic Acid Diethyla-mide," *New England Journal of Medicine*, Vol. 278 (Feb. 22, 1968), 435.

Louria, D. B. "LSD—A Medical Overview," *Saturday Review* (Apr. 22, 1967), 91-92.

Louria, D. C., T. Hensle and J. Rose. "The Major Medical Complications of Heroin Addiction," *Annals of Internal Medicine*, Vol. 67 (July, 1967), 1-22.

McGlothlin, W. H. "Hallucinogenic Drugs: A Perspective with Special Reference to Peyote and Cannabis," *Psychedelic Review*, No. 6 (1965), 16-57.

McGlothlin, W. H., S. Cohen and M. S. McGlothlin. "Long-lasting Effects of LSD in Normals," *Archives of General Psychiatry*, Vol. 17 (1967), 521-532.

Milman, D. H. "An Untoward Reaction to Accidental Inges-tion of LSD in a Five-Year-Old Girl," *Journal of the American Medical Association*, Vol. 201 (1967), 821.

Murphy, H. B. M. "The Cannabis Habit: A Review of Recent Psychiatric Literature," *United Nations Bulletin on Nar-cotics*, Vol. 15 (1963), 15.

Osewald, I. and V. R. Thacore. "Amphetamine and Phenmet-razine Addiction," *British Medical Journal*, Vol. 2 (1963), 427.

Pahnke, W. N. and W. A. Richards. "Implications of LSD and Experimental Mysticism," *Journal of Religion and Health*, Vol. 5 (July, 1966), 3.

Press, E. and A. K. Done. "Solvent Sniffing: Physiologic Ef-fects and Community Control Measures for Intoxication from the Intentional Inhalation of Organic Solvents," *Pediatrics*, Vol. 39 (March, 1967), 451; (April, 1967), 611.

Robins, L. N. and G. E. Murphy. "Drug Use in a Normal Population of Young Negro Men," *American Journal of Public Health*, Vol. 57 (1967), 1580.

Scher, J. "Patterns and Profiles of Addiction and Drug Abuse," *Archives of General Psychiatry*, Vol. 15 (1966), 539.

Snyder, S. H., L. Faillace and L. Hollister. "2,5-Dimethoxy-4-methylamphetamine (STP): A New Hallucinogenic Drug," *Science*, Vol. 158 (November, 1967), 669-670.

Solursh, L. P. and W. R. Clement. "Hallucinogenic Drug

Abuse," *Canadian Medical Association Journal,* Vol. 98 (1968), 407.

Teitelbaum, D. T. "Stramonium Poisoning in 'Teeny-Boppers,'" *Annals of Internal Medicine,* Vol. 68 (1968), 174.

Ungerleider, J. T., D. D. Fisher and M. Fuller. "The Dangers of LSD," *Journal of the American Medical Association,* Vol. 197 (1966), 389-392.

Unwin, J. R. "Illicit Drug Use among Canadian Youth," *Canadian Medical Association Journal,* Vol. 98 (1968), 402.

Vaillant, G. E. "A Twelve-Year Follow-Up of New York Narcotic Addicts," *American Journal of Psychiatry,* Vol. 122 (1966), 727.

Weil, A. T. "The Use of Nutmeg as a Psychotopic Agent," *United Nations Bulletin on Narcotics,* Vol. 18, No. 4 (1966), 15.

Winick, C. "Maturing Out of Narcotic Addiction," *United Nations Bulletin on Narcotics,* Vol. 14 (1962), 1.

ABOUT THE AUTHOR

DONALD B. LOURIA, M.D., is a graduate of Harvard College and the Harvard University Medical School. From 1955–1957 he served as an assistant surgeon with the United States Public Health Service. In 1957 he became a full-time teaching staff member of the Cornell University Medical College in New York City, and is currently an associate professor of medicine.

Dr. Louria is the President of the New York State Council on Drug Addiction, Professor and Chairman of the Department of Public Health and Preventive Medicine, New Jersey College of Medicine and Dentistry and is the co-author, with Mel Sokolow, of *Nightmare Drugs*. He is also the author of articles on the drug problem published in THE NEW YORK TIMES MAGAZINE and READER'S DIGEST.

He and his wife and three children live in Summit, New Jersey.